The Application
of Systems Analysis to
Government Operations

PRAEGER SPECIAL STUDIES IN
U.S. ECONOMIC AND SOCIAL DEVELOPMENT

The Application of Systems Analysis to Government Operations

Guy Black

FREDERICK A. PRAEGER, Publishers
New York · Washington · London

The purpose of the Praeger Special Studies is to make specialized research monographs in U.S. and international economics and politics available to the academic, business, and government communities. For further information, write to the Special Projects Division, Frederick A. Praeger, Publishers, 111 Fourth Avenue, New York, N.Y. 10003.

FREDERICK A. PRAEGER, PUBLISHERS
111 Fourth Avenue, New York, N.Y. 10003, U.S.A.
5, Cromwell Place, London S.W.7, England

Published in the United States of America in 1968
by Frederick A. Praeger, Inc., Publishers

Second printing, 1969

Library of Congress Catalog Card Number: 68-18914

Printed in the United States of America

PREFACE

This book is intended for the large group of
persons, not themselves systems practitioners, who
may have developed a curiosity about the systems
approach, or have been put in the position of
needing to exercise personal judgment as to its
applicability to particular operations of governments. The typical reader whom I had in mind was
a trained and experienced professional person,
occupying a high or middle management level in
government, and involved in a program or activity
for which systems approaches had been suggested.
I have considered what difficulties would such
persons have in understanding what is meant by the
systems approach as applied to their activity; how
they could protect themselves from being oversold
or being led to approval of a particular approach
or performer that would in fact be inadequate.

Such persons have many problem in assimilating
the systems approach. Their efforts at self-education
through attendance at conferences and meetings, or
in reading the simplified and propagandistic literature which dominates the popular and semitechnical
journals will not be of much help, and neither will
the highly technical literature of the engineers,
mathematicians, cyberneticists, or operations
researchers.

The gap which this book is intended to fill
lies between the overly popular and the highly
technical. The readers are supposed to have analytical competences of their own, and a sophistication in a spectrum of analytical methodologies
which will enable them to grasp the implications
of the systems methodology with far more ease than
the person without analytical training. I have

taken advantage of this presumed background in pitching the level of complexity and detail in the text. My audience is, therefore, public administrators, nonsystems types with the capacity for digesting analyses, and even systems types who would like to evaluate their own perspective.

Casual readers of the literature on the systems approach are likely to confuse its principal elements; their close interrelationship makes this easy to do. systems analysis, particularly appropriate to cost-effectiveness analysis, has been recommended as a tool in a program budget. The concept of a program budget, as outlined in the 1949 budgeting and accounting report by the Hoover Commission, pointed out that program budgets would expedite executive and legislative reviews on two principal counts: first, on the desirable magnitude of any major government program of function in terms of need, relation to other programs and proportion of total government expenditures; second by identifying the most efficient and economical of possible arrangements of the work.

It is insufficient to consider systems analysis to be merely a generic name for a collection of techniques. A meaningful integration of a body of analyses directed to the design and implementation of a system is essential in any real systems analysis. The purpose of this book is to show the relationship between the tools of systems analysis and the structure of systems concepts as related to government operations.

The systems approach is often considered in conjunction with the Planning-Programming-Budgeting System. Program budgeting and the systems approach, therefore, have an affinity for each other. Program packaging simplifies the comparisons of efforts with similar objectives and means. Perhaps the recommendations of the Hoover Commission were premature, given the complexity of Federal Government functions and the status of systems capability at the time. Experience with broad systems concepts was then rare. Since then, it has developed mightily.

During my tenure as executive secretary of the President's Committee on the Economic Impact of Defense and Disarmament, I became aware of the difficulty in communicating between systems practitioners and government personnel who were not familiar with systems approaches. One result--a perfectly natural and defensible one--was widespread reservations as to the approach. Being convinced of the real merit of systems approaches where properly applied and that a proper exposition could help close the gap, I undertook to write a short article explaining the application of the systems approach to government operations. The reception of this article led me to expand it into this book. In the process of producing it, I have benefited from the opportunity to exchange views with more individuals than can easily be mentioned, but I would like to acknowledge especially the thoughtful criticisms of Melvin L. Upchurch, Administrator of the Economic Research Service of the Department of Agriculture, and my colleague in the Program of Policy Studies in Science and Technology of The George Washington University, Clarence H. Danhof. I would like, in a general way, to acknowledge the helpfulness of many people in industrial organizations with some systems competence, including, particularly, my former colleagues in Sylvania Electronic Systems, who often made me the recipient of a much appreciated person-to-person education, of a quality which is not easily matched in the university.

Guy Black

Washington, D. C.
May 8, 1968

CONTENTS

LIST OF FIGURES AND TABLES

FIGURES

TABLE

The Application
of Systems Analysis to
Government Operations

CHAPTER 1   THE PLACE OF SYSTEMS ANALYSIS IN GOVERNMENT

THE CURRENT INTEREST IN THE SYSTEMS APPROACH

"Systems approach" is a phrase with wide appeal. It suggests the panoply of science, a meaningful integration of activities potentially at cross purposes, and spectacular programs of large size. Perhaps it is sometimes hoped that a little of aerospace success and glitter will rub off onto more mundane programs if the threads of the systems approach can be picked up. One is sometimes reminded of the "Cargo cult" of Melanesia, whose members built mock airfields, control towers, and airplanes, in the hope that they could magically bring back the flow of goodies enjoyed during World War II.

But the systems approach is not magic. Though some explanations reek of a mystique, others fall back on the definition endemic to many professionals, that profession X is what X-ists do. Others describe the bricks and mortar of systems analysis and systems management but not the structure of which they are part. The frustration facing the administrator who seeks to form a judgment as to what a systems approach may offer is a serious obstacle to widespread realization of the potential of the systems approach. Since it is inherent in systems work that relatively few of those whose efforts are integrated by systems management are involved in the over-all integration, analysis, or management of systems, persons who may legitimately claim experience with the systems approach may not themselves be very helpful.

Increasingly, persons with systems experience in space or defense applications are moving into nondefense government. The missions of departments of the Federal Government are being re-examined at an increasing pace. New departments have been created and old ones have been restructured. Closely related is the growing interest in the general mix of program packaging and budgeting, cost-effectiveness, and systems analysis. State and local governments are developing parallel interests. City governments have been restructured to meet program package structures.

The need is great for an understanding in depth of what these systems approaches entail, to what programs they are well adapted, and the prerequisites for their use.

Systems analysis cannot be the exclusive province of systems specialists. Expertise other than in systems and experience in subject area fields is not dispensable. A wealth of practical experience and analytical methods of some specialized discipline is essential in a systems approach, which supplements rather than replaces existing skills. A certain reluctance to embrace what appears to be a new fad is surely healthy. All analytical procedures have pitfalls. Those whose bailiwicks are being invaded by systems analysts may legitimately expect problems with the new systems applications. Not infrequently, these will result from the failure of systems analysts to take into account points on which the established experts could give useful advice. For the experts to do this, however, they must know what the systems analysts are about.

Administrators particularly have a need for successful communication with systems practitioners. It is they who must adapt technique to the broad purposes of their department or agency. They will have learned, for example, how assumptions often strongly affect the outcome of a study, and the pitfalls that beset those who fail to understand the analyses on which they base their conduct.

A principal purpose of this book is, therefore, to provide nonsystems analysts and administrators with some insight into the purposes which systems analysis can serve, its methods, pitfalls, and problems. It is hoped that it can serve as the basis for an improvement in communication and understanding between administrators and analysts.

There is a class of issues in public policy which has not been considered much in systems analyses conducted for defense purposes by aerospace companies. These are introduced, in the first instance, to show that systems analysts need not be blind to such considerations as external costs and benefits, multiplicity of objectives, and pricing policies to which the nondefense Federal executive will be sensitive. In some respects I have gone beyond the literature in my concept of the systems approach, strongly based on microeconomics, and adapted to social problems in the public arena. Through comments on these topics, I mean to show the aerospace-based systems analyst where he needs to broaden his analysis if he hopes to adapt his methods to a broader range of problems.

The conditions for expanding the application of systems capability in nondefense areas are currently very promising. Systems analysis, systems engineering, and systems management apparently have the potential of helping new programs get off to a good start. There is support for the transfer at high levels in government, and the diffusion of systems capability is going on apace.

Not the least of the forces making for the transfer in the Federal Government is the leadership in the Executive Office. A government-wide planning, programming, and budgeting system has been implemented by a Bureau of the Budget directive which requires department and agency heads to establish adequate central staffs for analysis, planning, programming, and budgeting, to structure their activities by broad categories or "packages," and to evolve comprehensive multiyear plans within the framework of that program structure. These programs are to be backed up by annual memoranda on each program category, which are to spell out program content, objectives, and goals, and compare the effectiveness and cost of alternative programs and expenditure levels. It is quite apparent that the Bureau of the Budget envisages a considerable increase in the analytical content that Federal agencies will use in developing their programs.

THE STRUCTURE OF THE SYSTEMS APPROACH

The systems approach is operational in the sense that it seeks to bring to fruition a complex result in which the interactions between major elements have been carefully worked out. The approach itself is complex: If "approach" is taken to mean the over-all process, several system-oriented specializations may be identified as part of it. Systems management itself, over-all in concept and facing different tasks as a program of system development, moves from conceptualization, to system analysis, to system engineering, to fruition as a functioning and hopefully optimized system, and is in some respects a special management concept. The managerial technique for organizing and managing the implementation of a new system may be the most important skill transferred from military systems experience.

While it would be misleading to offer a definition of the systems approach with any pretense that the suggested usage would be universal, whatever definition is offered must meet several criteria. First of all, it is not useful to describe as a systems approach whatever may be produced by a small team. Second, a useful definition must serve to distinguish some kinds of management of complex and large scale activity from others. The most useful bases for a distinction are the manner in which responsibility for the entire lifespan of design and implementation is concentrated.

In the systems approach, analysis is pervasive. Analytical support does not stop with the design of a system, but continues until the design is brought to fruition. Continuing analysis provides the means for continuous re-evaluation and rescheduling of an on-going program.

An important attribute of the systems approach is an approach to organizational control which comes to a head in the concept of a systems manager with responsibility cutting across functional responsibilities. This control is not merely broad, but exists for the entire lifespan of the system. In the manipulation of system design and implementation of system attributes, a systems manager can set aside many of the conflicts which would be typical where a system was being worked on by many groups for which some part of the system was only one of the many responsibilities. A lifespan responsibility gives meaning to an overview that takes into account the effect of design on eventual operations. Authority of such scope makes it meaningful to take into account broad-based trade-offs between system design, system operation, and system support, because the authority and responsibility exist to implement the findings of analysis.

The system approach thereby opens the door for a tremendous expansion of analytical activity, often of phases of design and management for which such analysis would otherwise have been only of academic interest. And analysts have responded to the opportunities. From applications of the systems approach, a body of tools has evolved. New theories, new applications of analytical techniques have proliferated. The techniques of economics, engineering, mathematics, science, operations research, and management science have been introduced into system analysis and to some extent integrated with each other. Systems analysis has been a focal point for interdisciplinary approaches. The resulting cross-fertilization has given tremendous impetus to many fields of intellectual activity. The power that this broad spectrum of tools has added to the systems approach has given it much of its strength. A haphazard and uncoordinated application of the tools does not, however, amount to a systems analysis. No effort is worth the name of "systems analysis" if it does not achieve an integrated result through the use of its special tools.

In short, it is insufficient to take the systems approach as merely a generic name for a collection of analytical techniques, or for any analysis that is

merely broad in scope. Without a meaningful integration of a body of analyses directed to the design and
implementation of a system, there is no systems analysis. Areas of specialized knowledge can be found with
a literature overburdened with microcosmic analyses
that bear little relationship to each other. Such a
body of knowledge, regardless of its breadth, unless
translated into unified solutions to complex problems
is not system oriented. In the context of established
disciplines, the systems engineering teams typically
show less detailed understanding of microproblems than
the established experts. Their contribution is the
integration of analyses into a consistent whole so that
in toto their approach supplies a firmer grasp of a
complexly structured problem.

By way of further explanation, consider in more
detail three major phases of the systems approach:
systems analysis, systems engineering, and systems
management.

Systems Analysis

Systems analysis, in many ways the touchstone of
the systems approach, is undertaken with a view to
identifying rational decisions as to the design, selection, or operation of a system. Ideally, analysis seeks
clear identification jointly of the one best system and
the most efficient way of operating it.

Much of the difficulty in describing the systems
approach is traceable to difficulties in describing
systems analysis. One impediment is confusion between
the process of systems analysis and the structure of a
systems analysis. The work habits and procedures of
systems analysts often display the disorder and confusion which are common with ill-defined problem assignments. However, a completed systems analysis will
generally be found to consist of major phases with a
meaningful relationship to each other. The pattern of
all systems analyses tends to have much the same structure, no matter how they are arrived at. In retrospect
it may be a thing of beauty, but one should not look at
the mess on the floor.

The first phase of a systems analysis is understanding and translating into analytically meaningful
terms the objectives that are sought by some as-yet-
undefined complex of equipment and/or activity, taking
into account the environment in which it is to operate.
Once these are understood, an analytical process can
be initiated that consists of:

1. the creation of an analytically manage-
    able model of the interrelations between
    major elements of the system and the
    external world;

2. quantification of functional relation-
    ships between rate of system operation
    and system "outputs";

3. quantification of functional relation-
    ships between rate of system operation
    and system "inputs";

4. the combination of (2) and (3) into an
    over-all input-output relationship that,
    submerging intermediate relationships
    within the structure of the model, expres-
    ses system outputs as a function of system
    inputs;

5. the determination from the input-output
    relationship of optimum system design
    and, rates of inputs and outputs that
    correspond to an optimum operation of
    that system.

A full systems analysis is feasible only when
each of the above steps is feasible. But partial
systems analyses may also be very useful. System
analytical techniques may narrow the need for intuitive approaches by providing hard information for
part, if not all, of a system problem.

Systems Engineering

Systems analysis seeks to create a broad framework of the system, taking into account that which

can be designed without going so far as to undertake
that design. System analysis selects performance
specifications from among those which engineers have
informed the analysts lie within the bounds of feasibility. There is a best way--often the least costly
way--of obtaining a performance result. Performance
specifications are not design specifications, however.
Systems analysis identifies the result wanted. Engineering is concerned with creating a design that incor-
porates the optimized technology.

Where a task is large, e.g., system-like, there
will be far too many design goals for any one engineering team to manage. Tasks must be subdivided and
assigned to various groups as one of the initial functions of systems engineering. After the system specifications have been selected through systems analysis,
systems engineering undertakes to divide the over-all
system design task into subtasks. It makes assignments
to various engineering groups so that each can operate
in a well-defined sphere where interaction with the
tasks of other groups is clear-cut and minimal. Groups
with such tasks need to take into account the manner in
which other groups fulfill their tasks only at points
of interaction with subsystems being designed by various groups. Systems engineering has been well done if,
after every task is completed according to specifications, the results can then be smoothly integrated into
an over-all working system. It will be seen at once
that this is precisely the criteria for subsystems as
elements of a well-conceived over-all system.

In the interests of time, many parts of a system
will be under design concurrently by different design
groups. How the products created by the various groups
interface with each other must be watched. System engineering performs this over-all coordinating role. It
may also take principal responsibility for some aspects
of design such as system weight, commonality of parts,
and reliability. As subsystem characteristics are
dynamic while design is underway, it must continually
evaluate the evolving system vis-à-vis the objectives
originally set and the preceding systems analysis.
During this phase, there may be some redoing of systems
analysis in support of systems engineering. Systems

engineering performs a continuing task of managing
and integrating the engineering phase of system
creation. These tasks continue throughout the
production of system hardware into system operation.

That the developmental effort on a system can
be directed principally at well-defined problems of
limited scope is a powerful advantage produced by
systems engineering. The vast bulk of engineering
in a systems development program is, therefore, not
systems engineering. A division of intellectual
labor is achieved with multifold benefits.

Systems Management

The systems manager has an over-all responsibility
that includes not only ordering and phasing systems
analysis and systems engineering, but the earlier
steps of monitoring the way in which systems analysts
interpret the customer's objectives, the way systems
engineers interpret the systems analysts' specifications, and the later steps of moving the completed
design from engineering to production, to testing, to
the development of supportive systems (e.g., a training program), to final use. He must schedule, control,
and press the system forward, locating the requisite
resources, resolving questions of priority, implementing coordination.

How systems management differs from other types
of management is most simply explained in the context
of the modern industrial organization. Consider for
the moment the flow of information and decision-making
in a hypothetical, extremely centralized, business
organization in which separate managerial hierarchies
have been established for each function--manufacturing,
sales, finance, research and development (R&D), etc.
The system concept of such an organization would show
vertical information and authority flows within each
functional hierarchy, and a cross-functional flow only
at the top. To achieve a lower-echelon coordination
between, say R&D and production, reports would have
to flow vertically to the top of the R&D production
hierarchy and then to the chief executive.

The unworkability of such an extreme is obvious. Management in business is typically decentralized to some degree--often by the creation of a hierarchy of general managers who exercise authority over all functional parts of the organization bound together by a common product interest or geography, and at a lower level than the chief executive. When a task that has the scope of a system is the focal point for such authority, systems management has been created--and we are faced with the essence of the systems management approach. Systems management is a special application of decentralized management as well as being a special type of consolidated responsibility.

That systems management extends over time has been noted. Today, the scope of Defense Department weapon-system concepts often includes not only equipment procurement--research, development, and production--but the mode of systems employment--staffing, training of personnel, logistic support, procurement of special related equipment and supplies, and strategy of employment. All of these may lie within the authority of a systems manager.

Not infrequently systems management is, in fact, superimposed on a management structure decentralized on some other basis. Systems efforts exceeding the capability of single companies or traditional military units have been on the scene for over a decade. Multi-company efforts for the production of systems under the systems managerial leadership of private contractors and program management offices within the Armed Forces have been particularly characteristic of aerospace weapon development, and aerospace has thus been identified with the systems approach.

CONCLUSION

By classifying phases of the systems approach, and systems analysis, an impression can be created erroneously that various phases are clearly distinguished, well defined. Only in exposition are the phases of the systems approach separate. A period of intensive systems analysis necessarily precedes systems engineering,

production or operation, which tapers off as systems
analysis continues in support of systems engineering
and systems management in the latter stages of a system program. Systems analysis requires as a prelude
to the intensive period, technical information on the
physical relationships on which system analyses are
based. This is a vital element of any analysis, which
engineering groups must supply. Some information
develops during the design process, or during operation,
so that systems analysis can and must be further refined,
reacting so as to effect perhaps the very engineering
groups that supplied the new information.

Much of the interest in the systems approach arises
from its characteristic effectiveness in high-technology
operations. Improvement in management techniques, associated in recent years with coordination on an unprece-
dented scale of weapon development, is surely the result
of forced-draft conditions and a climate favorable to
innovation. Systems analysis has been hospitable to
and has borrowed extensively from other disciplines,
including economics, engineering, and operations research.

Setting aside many important elaborations of method
for the purpose of exposition, the concept of systems
analysis, and some perspective on the problems associated
with it, can--I hope--be communicated by focusing on systems analysis in simple terms. There is merit in emphasizing the simpler methods: In fact, there is no tradition of analysis of system-wide scope for many socio-
economic activities of government. Much of value can
be accomplished without the more difficult techniques.

CHAPTER 2 CONCEPTS OF A SYSTEM

SYSTEM SCOPE

"System" is not a new word, coined as were "cybernetics" and "automation" to describe a new concept. One definition (<u>Barnhart American College Dictionary</u>) seems adequate: an assemblage of things or parts forming a complex or unitary whole. The scope of the examples illustrates the generality of the concept: a mountain system, a railroad system, a system of currency, a system of government, a penal system, the Copernican system, the nervous system. The Greek word for "organized whole," "systematize," is appropriately descriptive of the conceptual phase of the modern system approach.

It would seem necessary to answer the question, what is a system?, before approaching the questions, what is systems analysis?, systems engineering?, systems management? Arthur D. Hall defines a system as: "a set of objects with relationships between the objects and between their attributes."[1] This is satisfactory as far as it goes.

A system is a structure of subsystems. What then is the limit of aggregation that may still justifiably be called an organized whole, and what is the limit of disaggregation into subsystems? At one extreme, it stops where there is no unit which is usefully analyzed on a smaller scale. This is a limit of analytical convenience. The analysis of subsystems is, indeed, partly a means of simplifying the analysis of systems. But even the most atomistic subsystem, so long as it is

resource-using, must transform at least two inputs
into at least one output for there to be a meaningful
analytical problem.

Establishing scope and subsystem structure are
the tasks of system conceptualization--among the first
steps that must be undertaken when a problem of system-
like scope is approached. To direct analytical efforts
constructively, it is necessary to describe a problem
in a way that gives useful insights. A critical dimension of a problem is its <u>scope</u>. The initial investigation of a problem usually results in an awareness of a
tremendous complex of interrelated factors, some of
which are obviously important, and others where relevance is somewhat uncertain. In refining a problem
concept, irrelevant and secondary considerations are
gradually isolated to leave a hard core that is vital
not merely to problem understanding, but to a purpose-
ful attempt to solve it. Excluding the uncontrollable
as well as the trivial is an important part of developing a system concept. Until we can control weather, it
is part, not of a system, but of a system's environment,
no matter how critically it may affect system operation.

Often system boundaries are not easily defined,
there being no hard or fast rules as to what must be
considered as part of the system. The selection of a
boundary establishes the interface between the system
and the rest of the world. It should be selected in
such a way that system-world interaction is relatively
simple. By conceptualizing systems, systems analysts,
to some extent, select their problems. But they must
not do so merely to simplify their work at the expense
of its relevance.

The distinctions that affect the choice of a system boundary are, for example, always difficult in the
case of transportation studies. An analysis of the
transportation system of northeastern United States
might take note of population growth, highway conges-
tion, the financial difficulties and deteriorating
equipment of the railroads, the impact of such new
technology as 500-passenger airplanes and the super-
sonic transport, the highway accident rate, the incom-
petence with which automobiles are usually serviced,

and the eyesore of the auto junkyard. Coupling these
subjects would grant recognition to the fact that they
are, in a sense, part of a common problem, and would
imply that an integrated solution should be sought in
preference to approaching each point independently.

An early task is, then, to understand the interactions within the system as it is defined. Transportation is, indeed, a system of systems. The automobile
transportation component is itself a system including
highways, automobiles, automotive service facilities,
highway patrols, snow removal and maintenance crews,
and even the designers of highways and automobiles.
The highway designer has attuned his highway to the
characteristics of existing automobiles. The springs,
speed, and steering of the modern American car are
attuned to modern road surfaces, lane widths, and road
curvatures. Automobiles have become attuned to the
national economic system by being designed so that
frequent replacement rather than first-class maintenance is the rational choice of most owners, thereby
generating jobs in automobile factories where the efficiency of mass production is available, rather than in
repair shops.

To delineate a system is to decide what must be
included and what can be set aside. There must be criteria for establishing the boundaries, which are not a
question of physical reality, as there is in fact no
point at which any subset of activity ceases entirely
to react with the outside environment. However, the
complexity and strength of this interaction will depend
on boundaries chosen.

Whatever is not materially affected by the operation of the system can be clearly excluded, though if
they affect the system, and not vice versa, they are
clearly part of the system environment. Boundaries
can be chosen so that the structure of inputs to the
defined system, and outputs from it, are simplified.
Further, feedback of outputs to inputs can be contained
principally within the defined system.

If the above boundary is called extensive, there
is also an intensive boundary. This serves to exclude

things that, although within the system concept, do
not significantly affect either system design or operation, and are safely ignored in system analysis. Assume
that the general objective is a system that will produce
a desired result with minimum resources. Those system
elements that by their magnitude or the extent of their
interactions with other elements have a significant
potential impact on cost should be considered for inclusion in the system. Ball-park estimates of major elements of automobile subsystem cost on a per mile traveled
basis might be obtained from rough estimates perhaps as
follows:

road (i.e., taxes and tolls)	2 cents
gasoline and oil	1-1/2 cents
tires	1/2 cent
injury and damage (insurance and repair)	2 cents
vehicle usage (depreciation)	5 cents
driver's wages	4 cents
maintenance	2 cents
surveillance and safety (police)	1/4 cent
	17-1/4 cents

While surveillance and tire costs are low they should
not be forgotten, as changes in their characteristics
might materially affect injury and damage costs, for
example. An awareness of the manner in which elements
interact, not merely with each other, but with the
environment, is necessary. For example, personal injury may be a function of speed, vehicle density on
roadways, vehicle design characteristics, highway
design characteristics, driver training, visibility
conditions. With regard to each, we need to explore
the range of possible values and the sensitivity of
other system elements to any particular value. We
need to distinguish characteristics of the environment
and of the system for which the selection of certain
values is critical. A characteristic that cannot
change, or one that may change with no effect, may
be excluded as a variable in a system model, regardless
of its importance from a philosophical point of view.

After a similar structuring and selection has been accomplished on the benefit side, an attempt can be made to evolve an over-all system concept. It is often useful at this point to present a model as a block diagram of elements showing interconnections between them, some elements supplying inputs for others, and receiving inputs from others and from outside the system. Some inputs, e.g., of capital plant, will affect the way in which other inputs are transformed into outputs.

OTHER SYSTEM CONCEPTS

In the chapters following, the discussion focuses principally on analytical concepts that were originally developed in economics, which seeks to design a system that produces results with an efficient use of resources. Some other analytical approaches might be noted at this point. Frequently these can be integrated with economics-oriented methodology.

Systems in Systems and Procedures Analysis

The special field known as "systems and procedures" is a distinct professional specialty. It has not adopted the terminology of cost-benefit analysis, though it seeks economy in the use of resources, particularly of manpower, an optimized balance between manpower equipment, an optimized configuration of equipment and organization of work. Material processing and flow was the characteristic focus of the work-methods type of industrial engineering. When attention was first directed to the handling of reports-- taking account of their content and their physical flow-- systems and procedures work developed as a new specialty. Systems and procedures is generally limited in intent and subject matter to the organization and flow of information.

The typical systems and procedures analysis is oriented toward the flow of information that supports routine decisions about operations. It explores the information relevant to those decisions, and seeks to supply decision-makers routinely with information needed to

make optional decisions. In such analysis, the system
concept commonly takes the form of a procedure chart
which is a process analysis detailing the flow of paperwork from out-baskets to in-baskets, the content of the
paper, and its relation to organizational structure.
Diagramming may use the symbols conventional in industrial engineering for operations, transportation, inspection, delay, and storage. Some of what systems and procedures lacks in glamour, it makes up in experience.
The well-defined techniques of systems and procedures
analysis are surely a natural result of experience and
an older analytical tradition. By comparison, the systems analyses of aerospace often show much of the disorder and immaturity of a still-young profession.

While systems and procedures is not to be accepted
literally as a guide for general system analysis, its
methods surely have much in common with general systems
analytical procedures. As the scope of the typical systems and procedures problem is relatively limited, and
the analytical problems are of modest proportions, they
can provide a useful introduction to general systems
analysis.

Systems in Data Processing Analysis

Data processing system concepts de-emphasize the
physical flow of paperwork by emphasizing the information content. Data processing has become virtually
synonymous with use of computers. Systems for computers
involve, on the one hand, the information systems of an
organization, and, on the other, the internal organization of computers.

Analysts oriented toward computer usage have expanded the theoretical content of systems and procedures
work. They have, for example, introduced concepts from
communication theory. Central to this theory is the
concept that what qualifies as information is the significance derived from data. A volume of detail which
reports no change when none should be expected does not
qualify as information. For example, if gross national
product normally increased 2 per cent per quarter, the
information content in a report on gross national product

would be the deviation from this expectation. To
qualify as information, deviations must be random,
since systematic deviations are predictable.

By extracting information from noninformation,
computer-based information systems seek to economize
on decision-makers' time and reduce the flow of non-
information. The analysis of information systems
tends, in practice, to broaden out. There is a trade-
off between the benefit an organization derives from
various uses of top management time--reading routine
reports, routine decision-making, and the concentration on unusual, unique, and critical problems which
is implied by the concept of management by exception.
Information may be needed infrequently where change is
infrequent. The needed quantity of data, the number
and types of data, and the frequency of reports can
therefore be determined only with the aid of an analysis of an environment.

Feedback of information would affect the operations
reported by the data. The response of an organization
to its information system depends on the frequency of
reports, and the time lag between data origination and
the feedback signal. The longer the period between
reports, the more "out of control" an operation can
become.

The census is the classic example of an infrequent
report with a slow-response time. Yet the apportion-
ment of Congressional districts does flow from census
reports, and Federal and state funds are often allocated according to population. Changing circumstances
have rendered a ten-year census interval too infrequent
for current decision-making.

Computer systems may be designed to control operations directly without human intervention instead of
merely providing information for a human controller.
This is relatively easy where the decision is routine,
and computers can routinely perform complex analyses
of several streams of data to generate a quite sophisticated output signal. Trends in computer system design
thus push data processing systems analysis closer to
general systems analysis.

The internal organization of computers is integral
with the organization's information system, since interactions proceed through the computer's input-output
devices. In a sense, the initial choice among available
computers is a selection of characteristics of the
information system.

Computers differ in such capabilities as memory,
arithmetic and logic operations, capacity and speed.
These characteristics are suitable material for cost-
benefit analysis, and data processing system studies
sometimes undertake cost-effectiveness analysis of
such characteristics. A measure of computer performance is "bits per second." For example, one computer
memory might store 1 million bits of information and
provide access to any single bit in a one-hundred-
thousandth of a second. This could be done by putting
all of the information into core memory where it is
highly accessible but very expensive to store. A drum
or disc memory, which would be less expensive, would
also provide read-out more slowly. Tape memory, which
is still less expensive, would provide the information
even more slowly.

Computer input-output devices are chosen on a cost-
trade basis. For example, a computer used for scientific
purposes typically computes a great deal to generate
little output so that slow-speed input-output options
are a sensible choice. Business systems more often
perform simple calculations on a large volume of data
leading to emphasis on high speed input-output devices.

The over-all capacity of a computer may be chosen
to meet an occasional heavy demand, leaving large periods
for which marginal cost of additional computing is very
low. The battle between specialization versus general-
purpose computers has been mostly resolved in favor of
the general-purpose machine--in large measure to take
advantage of this flexibility, though reinforced by the
price advantage of general-purpose types which stems
from the economy of longer production runs for computer
manufacturers.

Information processing systems are a clear necessity for many government operations; indeed the provision

of information is one of the principal functions of
many government agencies. Information systems are
logical candidates for systems analysis. One of
four systems analyses contracts let to aerospace companies by the state of California in 1965 to explore
the applicability of their methods in nonaerospace
work was indeed for an information system.

Cybernetics as a System Concept

Cybernetics is Norbert Weiner's science of communication and control in complex organisms.[2] It has
been called the art of steersmanship. It achieves the
generality attendant to a high degree of abstraction,
and its concepts are often strikingly parallel to system concepts that have grown up independently in such
diverse areas as the biologist's concern for the nervous system, the sociologist's concern for society,
the army officer's or the businessman's concern for
the control of his organization. By its generality
it has served to unify independent investigations into
system behavior and to serve as a bridge for the flow
of information between specialities. Its claim as the
foundation of any systems approach may be accepted if
one recognizes that cybernetics is also a synthesis of
system concepts from many disciplines. Beyond that,
however, Weiner has made important original contributions to communication and control theories which are
closely allied to cybernetics, if not part of it.

Cybernetics is abstract and conceptual, and deals
with the relationship between a system of entities,
whose relationships with each other it can describe
in mathematics. Thus, it presupposes a systems approach.
It focuses on the behavior of the system as a whole, and
particularly on the way in which the performance of the
system as a whole is affected by the presence of feedback effects. Positive feedback often increases error
or results in unstable operations.

Industrial Dynamics System Concepts

Industrial dynamics is a special type of systems analysis, introduced by Jay W. Forrester of the Massachusetts Institute of Technology, and derived rather directly from electrical servo-mechanism theory and design practice. This elaborate and sophisticated body of theory has developed rapidly since 1940 in response to the need for electronic and control systems in advanced weaponry.

Industrial dynamics views decision-making and the control that flows from decisions as the key elements in behavior of an organization. It is applicable to either systems in being or hypothesized systems and hence serves either as a descriptive or a design tool. Analytically, it produces information about the operation of the system over a period of time. The operation of several systems over time can be compared. The inherent criteria in industrial dynamics for identifying one system as better than another are stabilization and response accuracy criteria.

Systems as a Special Subject in Economics

One should not be misled by the extensive use made of microstatic economics in systems analysis to believe that economic systems as a specialty of economists is part of or closely related to the systems approach.

The study of comparative economic systems as a well-established subject in economics, generally consists of comparative analysis of substantially different systems in being, such as the private enterprise capitalist system of the U.S. and various socialist or Communist systems. Comparisons have also been drawn between countries at various stages of economic development, thereby gaining some insight into the dynamics of economic development.

In their own bailiwick, macroeconomists have evolved rather substantial system concepts. Another class of economic system models is derived from the input-output technique invented by Professor Leontief.[3]   The utility of these system concepts in support of economic policy is clear and they are approaches to analysis of how to operate economic systems in an optimum way.

The general lack of communication between general systems analysis and economics systems types makes it hard to judge the degree to which general systems analysis and the study of economic systems could be mutually supporting. In one sense, economics has always been a systems science, but most system thinking by economists is out of touch with that of general systems analysts. It is, of course, not merely economists who worry about society as a system: Cultural anthropologists, sociologists, historians, philosophers, and preachers have had quite a lot to say. They have approached systems concepts far exceeding what general systems analysts from hard science disciplines have presumed to tackle.

CONCLUSION

Perhaps the outstanding common feature of the various systems approaches is an expanded awareness of the possibility of conceptualizing complexes of activities as systems, of gaining operational and analytical advantages in doing so.

Taking a cross-functional point of view may greatly enhance the power and effectiveness of analysis, by bringing within the scope of analysis interactions that previously had been considered out-of-bounds. The very act of broadening problems complicates decision-making to the point of making systems analysis an absolutely essential element of the systems approach. Problems have not actually become more complex; rather, a capability has developed for taking more adequate account of complexity that always existed.

NOTES TO CHAPTER 2

[1]Arthur D. Hall, _A Methodology for Systems Engineering_ (New York: D. Van Nostrand Co., 1962), p. 60.

[2]W. Ross Ashby, <u>An Introduction to Cybernetics</u> (New York: John Wiley & Sons, Inc., Science Editions, 1963), is a good general introduction to cybernetics.

[3]William H. Miernyk, <u>The Elements of Input-Output Analysis</u> (New York: Random House, Inc., 1965), pp. 30-57.

CHAPTER 3

METHODS OF

SYSTEM ANALYSIS

Systems analysis encompasses: (1) establishing optimum system characteristics, (2) selecting a combination of subsystems that will in total comprise the desired system, (3) analyzing interactions between subsystems of a large system, and (4) establishing the characteristics of the subsystems. The last of these is fundamental, and is a microcosm of the larger analysis.

The electrical engineer sometimes thinks in terms of a "black box"--a pedagogical concept for a unit about which all that is known is what goes in and what comes out. A student may be asked to design contents that meet stated input-output specifications. But later in his career he may be given a more complicated black box problem in earnest, when a systems engineering group assigns design criteria for a subsystem as if it were a black box. The engineer must design the contents that produce the required transformation. Beyond this, he must produce a best design--often the least-cost design.

SYSTEMS AND SUBSYSTEMS

It is most useful, in the analysis of multiunit systems, to have in hand analytical expressions that express for all possible subsystems outputs as a function of their inputs, without reference to their internal content. Once these expressions are available, the next stage of system design consists of selecting from the catalog of subsystems those whose input-output functions fit together as an over-all system with desired characteristics. The resulting combination will itself have inputs and outputs which can be related to each other--and in which interactions that are purely internal to the combination drop from sight.

By this process, the specification of an optimum system proceeds in orderly discrete steps in which much detail becomes irrelevant to the later stages of the analysis. But this detail is not forever lost or set aside. Once general specifications of the over-all system are finally agreed on, the background of detail is the source of specifications for internal subsystem components.

An example will make this process more concrete. One subsystem of a home hi-fi system is the amplifier. Its inputs include a signal from phonograph pickups, power from a wall outlet. Another is a flow of repair services--labor and spare parts. Its outputs are an amplified signal which replicates the input signal, heat, and wornout parts. These outputs have different values to the user; indeed some even have negative values. Given costs of the inputs and values of the outputs, the engineer seeks a best possible design for the amplifier from his instructions as to costs of inputs, and output requirements. Specifically, he may seek that amplifier which will give ten watts output at the least cost per year, gets no hotter than 100° F and needs repair no oftener than yearly. His design function consists of selecting one of the possible technical approaches, making trade-offs between different tube types, circuits, and so on. Ultimately, he produces a design which will cost a certain number of dollars and produce ten watts of audio power and other outputs.

But perhaps the manager who originally requested a ten-watt-output design finds the cost not to his expectations. The engineer may then be asked to design eight- and twelve-watt amplifiers, and indeed even others. Let us suppose that after this design work, the engineer prepared a summary of the relevant input and output details of all the designs. The manager would use this--and no more--as information in selecting amplifier specifications for a whole hi-fi system. His next level of integration would be selecting a combination of an amplifier and loud speaker, using a similar summary from the loudspeaker engineer. With the two summaries in hand, the manager--in this case acting as a systems analyst-- would seek an optimum, making use of both sets of input-output functions. He would take into account the relevance of alternative mixes of inputs and outputs, e.g., how hot the amplifier became and its projected repair requirements. Finally, he would expand his analysis to encompass the whole system.

After system components and the specific inputs and outputs were selected, the engineers would be requested to provide the detail behind the summaries so as to give the development staff more detailed specifications of the amplifier, etc., that is to be part of the system as it was finally settled on, and now must be more completely designed. The point of this illustration is to show that systems analysis is rooted in an enormous detail of subsystem analysis in which subsystem engineers optimize the portion of a system which is their responsibility, and by having done this, enable a system engineer to optimize, in simpler terms, the system as a whole. For systems analysts to arrive at optimum system specifications, however, the subsystems analysts must have this capability also.

TYPES OF SUBSYSTEM ANALYSIS

Economic Characteristics of Systems

The following three chapters concentrate on the analysis of systems by techniques closely akin to those of neoclassical economics, which will not be described at this point. While not the only one, the marginal analysis of economics is one method of identifying optimum subsystems designs. The analogy between a business firm and government-operated systems directed at the ends of society is sufficiently appropriate so that the theory of the firm is often relevant to public policy. Two major aspects of this theory are: (1) how a firm's behavior is affected by the demand for its output, and (2) how a firm uses resources to create that output. To apply this theory to system analysis in government, an analogy must be accepted between the revenue received by a firm from sale of its product

and a benefit received as a result of operation of a
system by government. (Revenue is really only a special
kind of benefit.)

   In industry, the interaction between demand and
production depends on the degree to which the firm exercises market control. Microeconomics has much to say
about optimal behavior where the price a firm receives
for its product is not subject to its influence. This
condition may prevail where the firm is small relative
to the market, provided further that its product is in
no way unique. Under such conditions, the situation in
which marginal benefits are equal to marginal costs is
a social optimum as well as an optimum for the firm,
provided that there are no costs or benefits resulting
from the firm's action for which it does not receive
full reward, or bear full cost.

   This is a particularly bad assumption for governmental operations. Government tends to have an outright
or near monopoly in any activity in which it participates
at all. Government is large enough to influence the prices of resources by the quantity it uses. Further, its
policy decisions frequently influence prices--as for
example, subsidization of resource exploitation or special tax treatment--which then become capitalized into
the price placed on particular resources or rights.
Further, government has often taken responsibility for
an activity specifically because there are important
external benefits or costs. However, there is in microeconomics a very large body of theory applicable to
situations where market power exists, and this may often
be useful.

   K. E. Boulding has noted that marginal analysis has
the defects of being highly formal and not easy to implement.[1] It is often quite difficult to quantify the marginal rate of transformation of input into output or the
marginal rate of substitution of one input or output for
another. In general, average figures are more available
than marginal figures. Partly, this may be because the
information which is required to obtain marginal quantities can be derived only from observation of a range of
values, variables of a system, and of stability of its
parameters, that are not usually obtained in nature.

Cost-Benefit and Systems Analysis

The differences between cost-benefit analysis, cost-effectiveness analysis, and microeconomic system analysis are that the first two are primarily means of evaluating proposals for given system designs, whereas systems analysis treats the design parameters not as given but to be chosen. Cost-benefit analysis is generally applied to a specific proposed design over which the evaluator has little power except to approve or reject. He does this by making direct comparisons of cost and benefit measured in the same terms, which is almost invariably dollars. A set of proposals, not necessarily mutually exclusive, might be subjected to cost-benefit analysis, and ranked according to their net benefit. With a limited budget, a selection would be incorporated into a portfolio considered to yield the greatest possible net benefit. Especially where several benefits result that are not reducible to a common denominator with each other or with cost, the analysis may take the form of identifying the minimum cost to achieve some level of equivalent, if not identical, effectiveness.

As part of system analysis, a cost-benefit or cost-effectiveness analysis is always directed at mutually exclusive alternatives, in which a choice is made of the one system to perform a given task--which cannot be performed twice.

The procedures of cost-benefit comparison as a phase of systems analysis do not materially differ from procedures where only an approve-reject decision is to be made. In a systems-analytical effort, more attention would be given to the effects of incremental changes in costs and benefits that result from modification of equipment characteristics, since selection of characteristics is a principal purpose of the analysis. This distinction is not clear-cut, however, as even in a restricted cost-benefit analysis, the effect of operation at different levels on net benefit will commonly be calculated by incremental technique.

Engineering Analysis

Engineering and physical sciences contain a substantial body of theoretical material which has been developed either explicitly for system analysis or is otherwise relevant to it.

It is hardly possible to review all of this other than to note that explicit in the role of an engineer or a builder is his responsibility for efficient designs. It has been said that anyone can build a bridge, but it takes engineering skill to build a safe bridge with the minimum of materials.

It is perhaps fair to criticize much engineering work for the criteria by which it orients its designs. To a considerable degree these are generated by the engineering profession for its own guidance, and adherence to them is part of professional conduct. It is notorious that engineers differ from other groups with reference to aesthetic and social considerations in system design, e.g., ugly but cheap bridges and superhighways that are cheaper if they slice through the heart of a city. Systems analysis can be a mechanism for formally incorporating a broader position on social objectives into the practice of engineering design-- and of developing a more rational appreciation of efficiency from a social point of view on the part of engineers.

Information Theory

The statistical theory of communication is an outgrowth of the work of Professor Claude E. Shannon.[2] It takes account of the stochastic nature of the transmission of information, defining information in a special sense. Information exists only because of "randomness" in the messages transmitted: any predetermined element in it conveys nothing new. The significant attribute of a communication system is the amount of information that can be transmitted through it. This can be increased by avoiding the transmission of non-information. For a communication channel with given attributes, a system or technology can be selected that transmits information at a rate as close to the channel capacity as desired with as low a probability of error as may be specified, but these two are trade-offs with each other, and high efficiency is costly and complex. To achieve maximum use of channel capacity, it is necessary to code messages in an appropriate form. Poorly coded messages, such as human speech, make very inefficient use of channel capacity.

The concept of information systems is very general. It has been applied to such obvious examples as telephone, radio, libraries, and even beyond to automatic control, managerial control, and education. The substantial theoretic background and related analytical methods lend much analytical power to any system concept that can be treated as if it were a communication system. The method lends itself easily to identification of optima.

Game Theory

John von Neumann and Oskar Morgenstern's Theory of Games and Economic Behavior first attracted general interest to game theory, which focuses on mathematical models of conflict.[3] A game includes a set of players and a set of rules which outline the choices of action open to each player under all possible circumstances and the payoff to each player at the end of any play. Game types are specified in such terms as "two-person zero-sum games," meaning that there are two players and that the sum of the winnings plus the losses is always zero, as what one loses the other gains, nothing being either destroyed or introduced anew by the game. Game models have been used to analyze the benefit or lack of benefit from cooperative action, as for example, international arms races.

Game theory attempts to define an optimum strategy for a player from an analysis of his gain and loss under possible courses of action open to him taking account of all possible courses of action open to his opponent. A special kind of game is the "game against nature" in which the decision-maker has no information as to which of several states of nature might come to pass, (i.e., the probability of rain).

Decision Theory

Statistical decision theory is concerned with the choice among alternatives on the basis of unreliable information. Usually, specified benefits and cost are assigned to every possible combination of decision and physical situation associated with that decision which, together with an estimate of the probability of exact outcome, is the basis for the evaluation of the result of various possible decisions. Decision theory is a branch of applied statistics. Fundamental in it is the assumption that system variables are random in nature and are describable as random processes.

Activity Analysis

Under the procedures of activity analysis, mathematical models are created consisting of linear equations which relate the possible levels of various activities to the pattern of available resources. The feasibility of certain patterns can be established. The object of analysis is selection from among them, taking account of cost and resource availability. The problem becomes one of finding the least-cost or highest-output pattern consistent with the resource constraints. Usual analytical processes consist of programmed search for better or optimum solutions, each step followed by tests for optimality. Dynamic programming refers to the treatment of multistage processes, either continuous or stochastic.

Queuing Theory

Queues, Markov processes, and processes in inventory theory are all applications of probability theory. It may be desired to estimate the necessary size of a new facility, according to the maximum expected demand. But this maximum may be only an occasional occurrence. Given a stochastic description of arrival rates and information as to service times, the fluctuating length of a queue awaiting service can be described. This leads directly to an analysis as to optimal maximum

serving rate for the queue, taking into account the
cost of facilities of various sizes and the cost
associated with the delays in awaiting service.
Queuing theory has been applied to highway design.

Feedback Theory

It is characteristic of many systems for the
output to influence the input, usually with some delay,
and serving either to counteract or reinforce the
effect of the input. Feedback is often the source
of cyclical system performance. The effects of feedback are not only widespread but practically unavoid-
able. Complex systems may include a number of feedback loops, even loops within loops. The analysis
can be quite complex.

While there is little place for consideration
of feedback in an analytical scheme that analyzes a
system at a single point in time--seeking an optimum
balance at that time as the design objective--it is
important to recognize that systems produce their
benefits over an extended period of time. It is
hardly conceivable that any system would not, in its
lifetime, be influenced by changes in the system
environment. How the system adjusts to these changes
is very important; a complete system design must
provide for smooth, efficient transitions, achieved
through selection of internal system characteristics.
It is, indeed, possible to design inadvertently a
system that is inherently unstable--even without
changes in the environment.

Feedback theory is useful for the design of
dynamically stable systems, for systems that are
self-correcting, for systems that respond effectively
to changes in input signals. It is largely an engineering theory, but one that has tended to be applied
more broadly.

Adaptive and Learning Theory

An adaptive device is one which adjusts to changes
in the environment in order to maintain the level of

performance. The temperature compensation built into
timepieces is adaptive. An adaptive system will respond
to a change in environment in precisely the same way
upon successive trials.

A learning system will respond more precisely or
more quickly with each successive trial, as it is able
to evaluate, from past experience or behavior, a change
in environmental conditions. Learning therefore requires
a memory capacity, the extent of which determines the
ability to learn. The rate of learning may depend upon
the arrangements made for "reinforcement," i.e., rewards
for improved behavior.

SYSTEMS ANALYSIS AS AN INTERDISCIPLINARY EFFORT

Systems analysis is interdisciplinary only in a
special sense. Above all, systems analysis is not a
generic name for interdisciplinary efforts. Indeed,
many disciplines can, by the nature of systems analysis play only a peripheral role.

Disciplines that are formally directed toward
optimization, as are much of engineering, mathematics,
and economics, must always be central to systems analysis. The thrust of many behavioral and biological
sciences is directed at basic understanding (theory),
measurement and, at best, a somewhat hit-or-miss problem-
solving orientation. As such, they are well suited
to supplying, on the one hand, suggestions for the basic
framework of system analytical models, and on the other,
an ability to quantify many of the functional relationships in models, but they do not supply the analytical
machinery that makes systems analysis a reality.

What the systems analyst will demand from behavioral scientists is predictable: He will want to know,
for example, how many auto thefts will occur in a slum
of specified characteristics as a function of a number
of streetlights, frequency of police patrols, number
and size of youth recreation facilities, and so on.

The behavioral scientist may respond quite predic-
tably by pointing out that the data in this form do

not exist even approximately. He may reject the entire approach, in effect telling the systems analyst that his model is wrong, or that his objective function is naive. Such a challenge will oblige the systems analyst to improve his working knowledge of social science or learn to work effectively with social scientists.

Many disciplines that must contribute to social system concepts do not normally develop information in the form sought by systems analysts. Why should they? The analysts are not their usual audience. Even so, they often produce results which are adaptable to system purposes, and other results can be developed to fit a systems structure. Special bodies of knowledge have already evolved which are explicitly directed at providing biological or physiological information for use in engineering and systems analysis. Human engineers, for example, worry about chair and table heights, the placement of controls, and the form of instructions on control panels that are least likely to lead to mistakes. A more meaningful integration of analytical with descriptive science takes place where adaptation to the human function is central--not merely a refinement--as it is with the life-support system in a space capsule or an adaptive learning system based on electronic and associated hardware.

CREATIVITY AND SYSTEMS CONCEPTUALIZATION

The creativity attendant to system conceptualization has often been noted. Creativity and problem solving themselves have been studied and something is known of the characteristics of creative persons, of the types of organizations and environment most conducive to creativity.

Something is also known of how complex problems are solved. Well-learned responses to typical problems may be psychological traps which blind one to unusual-- but possible--approaches. The childhood puzzle which is solved by arranging familiar objects in an unfamiliar way has adult counterparts. The practitioner deeply immersed in his subject matter or analytical methodology is not the person most likely to come up with novel approaches.

Steps that might be taken to broaden the range
of approaches are suggested by the literature on
creativity and problem solving. They involve the
deliberate destruction of constraints and the employment of persons not overly tied to existing approaches.
The search for novel approaches should involve persons
with a wide variety of background, analytical experience, subject matter, expertise, and culture. For
example, the aerospace engineer may be put to work on
social problems. At the conceptual stage, his unfamil-
iarity with the social problem literature may be a
positive advantage.

It is not intended to say that the novel approach
is always better, but, at a very early stage of systems analysis, it is desirable to uncover as broad a
range of approaches as can be achieved. Obviously,
many will quickly be eliminated and the mortality
rate among really novel approaches should be expected
to be high.

Of course, it does no good to uncover novel
approaches if they are then rejected out-of-hand.
To undertake an adequate, serious, open-minded analysis
of an unusual approach is often annoying, emotionally
disturbing, and hard work.

Sociologists have noted that the type of person
who is highly receptive to innovation, who will champion
an innovation and champion it among his peers, is a
somewhat special breed of cat. Typical characteristics
are cosmopolitanism based on frequent intellectual
communication with a community that transcends the
bounds of his own organization. Another is a degree of
independence rooted in self-sufficiency or security.
For such a person an error is not a disaster, and his
cosmopolitanism isolates him from the hostility to
innovation of the more limited community. However,
if the early adapter of innovative ideas is not also
influential in his community, he cannot serve as a
channel for diffusion whatever his own receptivity.
Wealth or social position often gives innovators both
the prestige that protects them from any stigma attached
to undermining the existing order by innovation and a
degree of influence as well. Academics not infrequently
make use similarly of their security.

The attributes conducive to creativity or early advocacy of innovation may not be those best suited for later implementation. Organizations which do not allow for distinct specialization in conceptual and follow-through phases tend to see the resulting difficulties in this light: Some of its personnel are great on ideas but failures at follow-through; others, who do well on follow-through, never have other than second-rate ideas to follow through on. The solution of this dilemma is a proper division of labor between conceptualization and implementation, recognizing each as a distinct specialty. It is indeed characteristic of engineering training that it produces many persons who are skilled at solving well-defined problems, but poor at conceptualization; the problem identifier who can state a problem in such a way that the problem solver can come to grips with it successfully is a valuable person.

NOTES TO CHAPTER 3

[1] K.E. Boulding, "Economics," in Robert E. Machol, ed., System Engineering Handbook (New York: McGraw-Hill Book Company, 1965), pp. 35-1 to 35-3.

[2] An interesting discussion of communication theory is contained in J.R. Pierce, Symbols, Signals, and Noise (New York: Harper and Brothers, 1961),

[3] John von Neumann and Oskar Morgenstern, Theory of Games and Economic Behavior, 2nd ed. (New York: John Wiley & Sons, Inc., 1964.)

CHAPTER **4** BENEFIT FUNCTIONS

IN SYSTEMS ANALYSIS

THE BENEFIT QUESTION

Government programs are directed at producing public benefits. The measurement of benefits poses major difficulties in cost-benefit analysis. Often statistics associated with benefits suffer from some degree of irrelevancy, so that optimizing available statistical indicators of benefit may, in fact, fail in some degree to maximize benefits and may even work against them. In his article, "The Ethics of Rational Decision," Kenneth E. Boulding warned particularly of the misuse of indexes of social performance reduced to a single scale, when in fact the quality of performance was substantially more subtle and complicated.[1]

Multiple benefits can be represented as a vector, which presents the state of society as it is supplied with possible benefits. The vector is composed of many elements, each representing one particular benefit. The benefit from implementing a system is thus the difference between a vector of social well-being with the system, and a vector without it. Implementing a system is a vector transformation. In seeking new systems, we seek a broadened range of possible transformations. Given a system in which many transformations are possible, the system optimization problem is to seek out that transformation that produces the greatest net gain in benefits.

The very possibility of a general social benefit function for society as a whole is debatable. Assuming that it may exist, it is useful to consider a

37

four-fold classification of its elements as created
by two dichotomies. The first dichotomy, of internal
and external benefits, focuses on the fact that some
benefits lie outside the range of the decision-maker's
narrow interests. The other dichotomy is between
economic and noneconomic benefits. This classification is paralleled by a considerable difference in
the ability to measure benefits.

Direct economic benefits have been most often
used as guides to policy or as variables in cost-benefit
calculations. It is for these that data and methodology
are most advanced. The state of knowledge is probably
the next best in external economies and diseconomies
which have been rather intensively studied in connec-
tion with tax policy and subsidies. Somewhat less is
known of direct noneconomic social benefits. The
most difficult area is indirect social benefits or
disbenefits.

Bertram M. Gross has objected to the "economic
Philistinism" of the United States Government's present
statistical establishment.[2] As economic characteristics
of society are frequently more measureable than social
characteristics, they tend therefore to be used as measures of performance, and one result is probably a bias
toward improving economic performance at the expense of
fuzzier social goals.

Albert D. Biderman examined the goals set by the
President's Commission on National Goals in 1960 in
two major statistical series, Economic Indicators and
Health, Education and Welfare Trends.[3] Of eighty-
one domestic goals, data bearing on them in some way
or another were found for forty-eight. The goals
which were least adequately covered were arts and
sciences, technological change, living conditions.
The most complete coverage was in education, economic
growth, and health and welfare.

Even where benefit cannot be measured, some satisfactory indicator of benefits may be possible that
ranks activities by degree of benefit. A crude measure of benefit may, in fact, be all that will ever
be possible. Bauer has taken the position that we
would be wise to stay away from attempting precise

measurement of social phenomena in favor of a system
of social indicators, attempting, however, to eliminate
systematic biases in the indicators. The use of indicators is especially valuable where it can be presumed
that unmeasurable external benefits are proportionate
to measurable benefits, so that changes in the indicators are accurately indicative of changes in the total
benefit.

For purposes of managerial control, most organizations have created reporting systems which provide
a continuing flow of data on organizational performance,
frequently stated in terms of work done or results of
certain types. A police department might count the
number of arrests made, a health service the number
of code violations reported.

The benefit implications of performance measures
from operating statistics may be suspect, as what is
reported is not actually the benefit expected to accrue
from the activity. Through its inspection of food
processing plants, a health service creates the benefit
of sanitary food. Its success might be measured by
periodic examination of food in the hands of the public
through a sampling survey. Indeed, the greater the
success, the fewer violations should be found, so that
the number of violations reported, though a measure of
work activity, is not necessarily a good measure of
amount of benefit created.

A similar point might be made in regard to the
benefit of traffic safety, obtained by adherence to
traffic regulations. A periodic survey could be established to monitor the proportion of motorists who
signal turns, etc., which would serve as a measure
of the level of safe driving. The effectiveness of
a process cannot be established from input measures
alone, but only from a comparison of inputs and outputs.

MULTIPLE BENEFITS

Where one easily measurable benefit is produced
by a system, the analyst is lucky; the assumption traditional to microeconomics that profit, measured in

dollars, is the only result sought by business, has
this advantage. But increasingly, attention has been
directed at the complexity of the structure of benefits really sought. For government activities, this
structure is particularly complex and elusive.

A benefit function is the embodiment in a mathematical form of the structure of benefits. Great
care must be exercised as to how benefits are incorporated into a function so that it is a true measure
of the extent to which the complex of objectives is
achieved. For example, a ratio of total benefits to
the total cost is entirely different from net benefit
(the difference between total benefit and total cost)
or the ratio of an increment of benefit to an increment of cost. Maximizing a ratio of averages seldom
maximizes net benefit, although a ratio of increments
of output over corresponding increments of input is
the marginal cost in real terms of additional benefits,
a ratio which, for all possible ways of achieving an
incremental benefit, would be equal at the point where
an optimum allocation of resources had been obtained.

A common difficulty is that alternative technical
approaches to producing benefits usually will use
resources in different proportions and produce various
benefits in different proportions. Eating food produces benefits, for example. Perhaps 10 apples and
12 oranges are as beneficial as 8 apples and 15 oranges.
However, having determined this does not make it possible to compare the benefit of either combination
with the benefit from 20 apples and 24 oranges. Benefits are subject to diminishing returns--and not necessarily at the same rate for apples and oranges.
Identifying the least costly way of achieving either
one of two equivalent benefit levels is relatively
easy, but unless we can legitimately reduce all benefits to a common measure, it will not be possible to
compute the _extra_ benefit of the 20-24 combination
as compared to a 10-12 combination. Unless we can
compare benefits and costs, we will have difficulty
saying whether 10-12 or 20-24 gives the greater _net_
benefit.

The difficulty, that several quite different
benefits are produced with no fully valid ways of

quantifying them or even comparing them with each
other, is nearly universal. The indifference function
of economics is a graphic representation or mathematical formulation of the problem. A number of techniques
have been developed for quantifying these functions
experimentally. An indifference surface can sometimes
be established by asking a panel to assign over-all
ratings to alternatives which offer different benefits
in different degrees. Conceptually, if the number of
alternatives is large enough relative to the number
of benefit attributes, separate identification is a
mathematical possibility. But being psychological,
the number of benefit attributes is never known.

A less ambitious effort is to establish an ordering of total benefit of a number of alternatives by
forcing evaluators to make a large number of paired
choices. Where multiple objectives are not mutually
exclusive, comparisons are possible. A can be compared
with B, C, and D to see which gives the higher benefit.
We then know that A exceeds B + C + D or the reverse,
and taking the weight that should be assigned to A as
equal to one, have imposed a constraint on the combined
weights of B, C, and D. Next we can compare B with C
and D, to obtain another constraint, and so on. As a
result--_relative_ to the weight of A--the weights of B,
C, and D must fall within certain defined ranges in
order for the outcomes of all comparisons to be consistent. Note that no absolute values are assigned--only
values relative to the value of A.

Practical Multiple Benefit Functions

To create a benefit function, alternative benefits
must be specified and a means established for making
choices among them. This process is more commonly
found than might be supposed. One example is in the
evaluation of competitive proposals for research and
development.

Proposal evaluations are preceded by consideration of the attributes that will be looked for. For
example, these might be: contribution to basic knowledge, improvement of existing systems, creation of

entirely new systems, the possibility of new inventions, the prestige or technical leadership that might
result from successful completion of the project. A
decision would also be made as to how much weight should
be assigned to each attribute. Then reviewers would be
asked to examine each proposal and score it according
to its quality with reference to each attribute. The
weighted sum of scores would be taken as the measurement of over-all quality.

A typical result of this process would be that
some proposals would rank above others on some attributes but not on others. Only occasionally will one
project rank higher than on others on all attributes.
Thus, a trade-off between a higher score on some
attributes for one proposal and a higher score for
other attributes on the other would be indicated.

For example, the scores on two proposals might
look like this:

Attribute	Weight	Proposal 1	Proposal 2
Basic Knowledge	.1	7	2
New Systems Potential	.2	4	3
System Improvement Potential	.3	2	7
Invention Possibilities	.2	5	3
Technical Leadership	.2	5	1
Overall Score		4.1	3.7

and a preference for Project 1 would be indicated,
although there is a higher likelihood of system
improvement with Project 2, and the weighting seems
to indicate that system improvement potential is the
most important attribute. In this example, such a
rating procedure may have created more problems than
it solved, but it is a frequently used and often helpful way of evaluating objects by a multiple scale of
benefits. Presumably, in the above example, evaluators would be led to reconsider the weights assigned
to various benefits--a perfectly valid move if new
insight, from a confrontation with reality, has improved
their judgment.

Even without such an evaluation, the objectivity in such a procedure is partly an illusion. The scores assigned for each attribute are a psychological response to a stimulus. The response to a stimulus is a learned process. The reviewer has learned from past experience to associate success in R&D with the ways in which a proposer demonstrates familiarity with previous work, his physical and intellectual tools, his methodology, his previous training and successes. None of these are rigidly related to success and every evaluator will have learned to respond somewhat differently from a somewhat different experience.

The rating schedule shown above contains built-in rigidities that are not necessary. Numerical scores that evaluators assign need not, for example, increase linearly with the strength of an attribute. The score might increase as the logarithm of the stimulus, or at some nonproportionate rate. Given a knowledge of the nonlinearity of responses to stimuli, the strength of the stimulus could be adjusted by a transformation function.

Constant weights in effect say that there is a linear trade-off between two attributes, which is inconsistent with the concept of diminishing returns. Additional increments of benefit derived from additional increments of an attribute's intensity should carry successively less weight in a multiple benefit function, in order to reflect the phenomena of diminishing returns.

BENEFITS FOR GROUPS WITH DIFFERENT VALUE SYSTEMS

Fundamental to any system of social indicators is, of course, a broadly oriented system of social values. Such value systems have been attempted by Talcott Parsons, Clyde Kluckhohn, and, more recently, by Bertram Gross of Syracuse University.[4] Systems of values, of course, vary from society to society and among groups in society. Thus, Edward E. Furash found that younger businessmen were more enthusiastic about programs with a long-range payoff such as the space program than were older businessmen.[5] Poor people are more enthusiastic about equal distribution of wealth than rich people.

Whenever two or more persons compare the benefits
of alternatives, differences in their value systems
are likely to produce different ratings. Where the
rating is intended to be purely objective, the difference is simply error in measurement, but frequently
evaluators reflect differences in values to which
they are legitimately entitled: This is indeed the
fundamental mechanism of the democratic process, and
is a point where public program systems analysis may
deviate from private practice.

But, is it always certain that the result of
multiple ratings by parties with different systems of
values will produce an optimum choice? Consider a
form of paradox suggested by Kenneth J. Arrow a few
years back.[6] Assume that three negotiating parties
are asked to rate three possible outcomes of the
Vietnamese struggle by order of preference: A. The
U.S. spends $5 billion on economic assistance and
democracy prevails in South Vietnam; B. the U.S. spends
$500 million and a military dictatorship prevails;
C. the U.S. spends nothing and Communism prevails.
Three parties rate outcomes in order of preference
as follows:

	First	Second	Third
Best	A	B	C
Tolerable	B	C	A
Worst	C	A	B

Now, if C is unthinkable, and the preference
of two of the three parties will prevail, A would be
chosen over B. If A is impossible, B would be chosen
by two of three. But if B is eliminated, C would be
chosen over A. This is an inconsistent ordering since
A is preferred over B, B over C, but C over A. Where
fine gradations of preference are allowed, the paradox is dissipated, but the problem of obtaining a
valid benefit function among parties with different
systems of values is real enough to make it difficult
to specify one mix of results as clearly preferable
to another. Elaborate schemes for an over-all scoring

from the independently-arrived-at scores of a number
of judges have been developed, such as that used by
Donald C. Pelz and Frank M. Andrews to obtain a rank-
ing of the competence of members of engineering labora-
tories.[7] Another approach is to allow an interaction
between evaluators under controlled conditions. This
is one function of committees or legislative bodies.

BENEFIT AND RISK

Confounding the question of benefits from various
systems is the risk that the benefit may not materialize
at all. The most straightforward treatment of risk is
to measure benefits in terms of their expected values--
essentially the probability of receiving the benefit
times the amount of the benefit. In this way, a small
but fairly sure benefit (e.g., a probability of .7
times a score of 3) would outweigh an unlikely large
benefit (e.g., .2 times 9).

But this assumes a linearity in reaction to risk,
which is probably not good psychology. Another treatment is to include risk as one element in a linear
rating scale.

A more flexible treatment of risk was developed
first for the analysis of investment portfolios. Suppose many possible investments have the two dimensions
of risk and rate of return. Given an investor's trade-
off preference between these two characteristics, an
optimum internally consistent portfolio can be selected.
Typically, the optimum portfolio is composed of a fairly
small number of investments with quite different risk
and return attributes.

There are other situations in which a risk-benefit
trade-off must be made--for example, the selection of a
"portfolio" of research and development projects, or
the allocation of funds to eliminate roadside hazards
to motorists, where each hazard can be characterized
by a probability of causing an accident, likely damage
from the accident as well as cost to remove the hazard.

SOME BENEFIT ISSUES

Benefits in Human Life and Health

There are innumerable programs for which one
benefit is prolonged life expectancy. This touches
on some very difficult questions. First, how is a
man-year added to life expectancy to be compared with
the cost of obtaining it? Second, how are man-years
of different persons to be compared, and third, is a
man-year equally valuable regardless of how obtained?

Health programs add man-years to life expectancy
of both the young and the old. By saving the life of
a 38-year old man, perhaps 34 additional man-years
result; by saving the life of an infant, 68 years.
But is saving lives of infants two times as beneficial?
The difference is 34 years down the road, and benefits
are valued less when obtained in the distant future.

The view has been taken that a man's life can be
valued at the discounted value of his expected net
earnings. On this basis, the value of an infant life
is low, since his future earnings are discounted by
many years. The present value of an oldster's earnings is also low. The peak value of discounted earnings is reached in the mid-twenties, as is shown in
Figure 1. If present value of gross earnings is
taken as a standard of value of life, it cannot be
ignored that the value differs according to types of
persons. Women live longer, but earn less.

The essentially arbitrary and unsatisfactory
character of present value of earnings as a basis
for value of life should be obvious. It would be as
meaningful to take a hedonistic view, that the present
value of life is the discounted value of all future
consumption. This concept would produce a higher
value for infants, oldsters, and those on relief.
There is, in fact, little point to assigning a value
of human life in a systems analysis. However, it
is sometimes done because much of the available
analytical machinery requires that some value be
assigned to benefits in order to run through the
cost-benefit calculus.

FIGURE 1

Present Value of Lifetime Earnings: Amount by Sex and Discount Rate

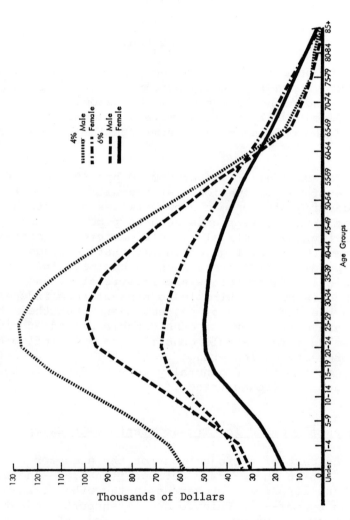

Source: Dorothy P. Rice. Estimating the Cost of Illness. p. 94.

47

To establish a trade-off between human life and
expenditure is a matter of value judgments expressed
by decision-makers individually or collectively. The
analysts may clarify their choices so that their decisions are rational in the light of their value judgments, but they cannot do this by bookkeeping concepts
of the values of future earnings.

System Use and Benefits

The benefit from a system depends on how much it
is used, which is often dependent on growth in population and economic activity. Occasionally, a system
improvement will itself stimulate economic activity,
as did the opening of a circumferential highway around
Boston.

Forecasting of use or demand has reached a fair
degree of sophistication. At the national level,
forecasting of economic growth relies on certain
rather predictable trends such as population and productivity, on relatively stable patterns of behavior
such as the percentage of income that is saved and on
less predictable factors such as business investment
decisions. These things are interrelated, and it is
not necessary or desirable to project them independently.
Since the durability of systems means that their benefits are derived over a considerable period of time,
system decisions should generally be most influenced
by forecasts of long-range trends. This is an advantage, as trends are generally more predictable than
fluctuations around trends.

Forecasted Demand for Transportation--An Example

As part of a projection for the need for transportation in the Chicago metropolitan area--and hence
the benefits from improvement in the urban transportation system--the Chicago Area Transportation Study
undertook to project the growth in population, in
production of goods and services, in income, and the
extent of land in the urban environment. As a starting place, it extrapolated a ratio of Illinois

population by assuming that the Census Bureau's projection of a declining ratio from 1960-70 would carry
forward to 1980. This led to an estimate of 9.5
million persons in the Chicago area in 1980. Next,
per-capita income was projected on the assumption
that productivity would increase by 1.8 per cent
per year, producing a 1980 income per consuming unit
of $11,300 in 1956 dollars. Changes were projected
in the pattern of consumer expenditures; one estimate
was that transportation expenditure would be 14.4
per cent of personal income.

To meet demand, production and employment would
increase. The pattern was estimated by a Leontief
type input-output model, adjusted by productivity
trends to arrive at employment; one projection was
for 1980 employment in "transportation, communications, and public utilities" for the metropolitan
area of 317 thousand persons.[8]

Finally, a 62 per cent increase in transportation expenditure was predicted for 1956-80. The
amount of this that would be spent on automobile
travel was then projected by relating automobile
ownership to income and the number of families in
various income groups. A forecast of over 3 million
vehicles in 1980 was arrived at--nearly twice the
1956 number, implying a near doubling of the miles
of automobile travel. This became the basis for
estimating the use to be made of highway systems and
hence benefits from improvements in the highway
system.

Benefits From Investment

Being composed of durable equipment, and therefore a capital investment, a system yields its benefits
over a period of time which follows and tends to be
longer than the period of investment in the system.
Thus, investments made now must be compared with
benefits obtained later.

That future benefits should be discounted at
some rate is widely understood. Thus, in a report
by the Department of Health, Education, and Welfare,

future costs of arthritis centers were discounted
at 0, 3, 4 and 10 per cent, the analyst disassociating
himself from the choice of a discount rate.[9]

Mathematically, the present value of a future
benefit, provided that it can legitimately be measured in dollars, is the amount that--invested today
at compound interest--would yield the equivalent
future stream of benefits at a comparable risk.
What this would be depends on the yield that whoever
might advance the funds would demand for comparably
risky investments. A low interest is appropriate
where the yield is certain, or the investment is not
much subject to the risk of obsolescence or accidental
loss of future benefit. It is quite reasonable to
apply different discount rates to various parts of
the overall investment in a system where some parts
involve more risk than others. Uncle Sam, as an
investor, incurs substantial risks as to whether the
benefits will materialize. For example, a regional
economic development program might use public funds
to finance public works, or on roads so as to encour-
age local economies. The history of such investments
is that many fail to produce the expected return.
As they are, therefore, high-risk types of investment,
a high discount rate should be used.

REDUCING THE VALUE JUDGMENT IN THE TECHNICAL PROBLEM

When the best way of achieving certain technical
results can be established, but no means of measuring
benefits from those results, another technique is
useful. This halfway house can be illustrated by
the problem of selecting enough spares for a new
electronic system to keep it operating without shutdowns. As failure of electronic parts is a random
event, there is always some finite probability that
any number of spare parts may be exhausted. But as
this probability can be reduced by buying more spares,
the point is to make the proper trade-off between
reducing the risk of not having spares and spending
more money on spare parts. If how much to spend so
as to avoid shutdowns due to parts shortage is a
value judgment, the analyst, as a technician, cannot

specify any particular risk without substituting his value judgment for that of the administrator who has final responsibility for the choice.

However, for a given expenditure on spares, the less chance of running out the better. And the analyst can determine how the least likelihood of running out can be achieved for a given expenditure. He does this by seeking the least-cost way of achieving a given result, e.g., a probability of shortage. He can repeat this for other levels of risk, and can combine all these determinations into a functional relationship in which the probability of adequacy of spares increases as a function of expenditure.

Here the technical phase of analysis reaches an end. The final step is a value judgment on expenditure versus probability of adequacy. Whoever makes that judgment has been relieved of any concern over the technical problem of design of spare parts kits. By providing an uncluttered view of the way in which risk declines as a function of optimally allocated expenditure, the technical analysis has been separated from the value judgment problem.

NOTES TO CHAPTER 4

[1]K.E. Boulding, "The Ethics of Rational Decision," _Management Science_, Vol. 12, No. 8 (February 1966), pp. B-161 to B-169.

[2]Bertram Gross in Raymond A. Bauer, ed., _Social Indicators_ (Cambridge, Mass.: Massachusetts Institute of Technology Press, 1966), p. 166.

[3]_Ibid._, pp. 86-97.

[4]Gross, _op. cit_.

[5]_Ibid._, p. 47.

[6]Kenneth J. Arrow, <u>Social Choice and Individual Values</u> (New York: John Wiley & Sons, Inc., 1951).

[7]Donald C. Pelz and Frank M. Andrews, "Evaluation of Performance," Appendix A in <u>Scientist in Organization</u> (New York: John Wiley & Sons, Inc., 1966), pp. 261-270.

[8]State of Illinois, <u>Chicago Area Transportation Study, Final Report</u>, Vol. IV (July 1960),

[9]Dorothy P. Rice, <u>Estimating the Cost of Illness</u>, U.S. Department of Health, Education, and Welfare, Health Economic Series, No. 6 (Washington, D.C.: U.S. Government Printing Office, 1966), p. 85-114.

5

THE SYSTEMS CONCEPT

AND COSTING

TECHNOLOGICAL RELATIONSHIPS

Systems achieve results through the use of
resources. The cost of those results is the sum of
their prices times the quantities used to create
and operate the system. Once a system is created,
the rate at which costs are incurred will depend
upon the rate of system operation, but this may have
been reduced by a larger expenditure on system creation.

As the operating rate of a system is varied,
the inputs of the various resources typically will
not vary proportionately to output, or to each other.
At one extreme are inputs that do not vary at all
as a function of the rate of output. Any use of
inputs to create outputs involves the use of previously created facilities--machinery or stock of some
kind. There could be no output without such resources,
but output per day from a given facility can vary
within broad limits, particularly by being operated
at less than a full shift where the machine operating
rate is technologically fixed.

Toward the other extreme are inputs that increase
exactly proportionate to outputs. Materials incorporated in manufactured goods tend to be of this sort.

Labor inputs and other materials, such as
electric power, tend to be intermediate in their
proportionality to output. If an increase in output
merely means precisely replicating the same work
operations, labor input would increase proportionately

to output. In small craft shops--tailors and cabinet-
makers--doubling the rate of output may mean two
craftsmen working independently side-by-side, creating
two suits or cabinets concurrently, and providing
the same input of man-hours per unit of output as
one man working alone. But in most productive operations involving manpower, some economy of human
effort can be achieved by reorganizing the work. If
one tailor concentrates on coats and the other on
pants, their productivity can be increased by this
specialization: that is, man-hours per unit of output decreases. As the size of a work force increases,
such opportunities become more frequent--up to a point.

It is the almost universal experience that,
under the circumstances where the facility and machinery stock is fixed in amount, a point is reached
where further increases in rate of labor input produce
proportionately less output per man-hour. This
phenomenon, widely known as "diminishing returns,"
is diagrammed in Figure 2A. All well-conceived
production operations operate in the region of
diminishing returns not merely for labor but for
all inputs. The meaningful question for the optimizer
is, have returns diminished to the point where they
would not justify the wages of an addition to the
rate of input? If an additional worker would still
produce output with a net return exceeding his wages,
to hire him is to increase net profit, otherwise
not; thus, the optimum rate of operation is at a
level of labor inputs where the increment of value
from that laborer has diminished to equal precisely
his wages. It will be seen that such an equilibrium
would never be reached at a rate of output characterized by increasing returns.

The above, of course, is from the marginal
analysis of microeconomics. It is rooted in the
physical and technological realities of any process
by which inputs are transformed into outputs. In
short, the organization of an input-output operation
is an economic question, not merely a technical one--
but one where neither the technological nor the
economic question can be resolved independently.

FIGURE 2

Characteristics of Technologies Transforming
Inputs into Outputs

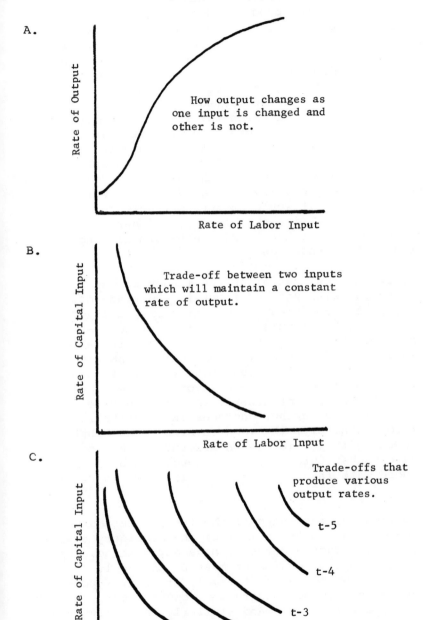

A.

Rate of Output

How output changes as
one input is changed and
other is not.

Rate of Labor Input

B.

Rate of Capital Input

Trade-off between two inputs
which will maintain a constant
rate of output.

Rate of Labor Input

C.

Rate of Capital Input

Trade-offs that
produce various
output rates.

t-5

t-4

t-3
t-2
t-1

Rate of Labor Input

While the above reasoning has been applied traditionally to the production operations of profit-oriented entrepreneurs, it is germane to a wide range of processes wherein various mixes of inputs are transformed into various mixes of outputs, and where the optimum technology and choice of inputs are sought. Increasing and then decreasing returns have been found to be duplicated for all types of inputs, if the rate at which one input is applied is varied while the rate of other inputs are held unchanged. That diminishing returns would be found with increases in the stock of tools and equipment, is particularly easy to see: If there were two tailors, output would jump quickly by providing them with one tailor's bench. It would be further increased but less than doubled with two benches, and hardly increased at all with a third bench--diminishing returns with a vengeance.

Quite as fundamental as the manner in which output varies with rate of input is the trade-off among inputs. Speaking in general terms, a trade-off between labor inputs and machinery inputs-- the consideration that in its modern form is called automation--is fundamental. The further one goes in seeking a given result through the substitution of machinery for labor, the less favorable the substitution ratio is for machinery. And the reverse is as correct: The further one goes in substituting labor for machinery, the less favorable the substitution ratio is for labor. A diagram of change of ratios of substitutability to produce output at an unchanged rate is curvilinear, as is shown in Figure 2B.

Obviously, the shape of the labor-input curve will depend on the technology of the machinery available, and for such a curve to have any meaning, the type and amount of equipment must be precisely specified. Indeed, a whole family of labor input-output curves can be constructed, one for every machinery combination. And similarly, a family of machinery input-output curves for all possible labor forces is possible. Further still, a family of labor-machinery trade-off curves can be constructed, one for each different level of output.

These three families of curves can be combined
into a single three-dimensional surface to show how
output increases with an increase in either input,
or both. In Figure 2C, vertical height is the level
of output, and along the two horizontal axes are
rates of labor and capital input (e.g., machinery),
respectively. If this surface is sliced in three
separate ways, parallel to each of the three axes,
a labor input-output curve, a capital input-output
curve and a capital-labor substitution curve will
stand revealed by the edges of the slices. Graphic
representation cannot go beyond three dimensions,
but any number of dimensions can be expressed mathematically. In this way, many of various grades of
labor, types of machinery, types of materials, types
of output can be separately represented. The mathematical form would incorporate the diminishing return
feature to every input and the increasingly unfavorable
trade-off to every input as it was increased in amount
relative to other inputs.

These are general principles, established from
general observation of productive activity, supported
by philosophical and theoretical principles, and
sometimes verified by experimentation (e.g., by varying
the quantity of fertilizer). One critical point in
all of this is still unsettled: how output will
vary if all inputs are increased proportionately--
in short, as the scale of a combination of inputs is
increased. Some studies have suggested that output
tends to increase exactly proportionately to inputs
increased in the same proportion to each other.
Sometimes there appears to be increasing returns to
scale--sometimes decreasing, but usually only to a
slight degree.

Considerable use has been made of these general
principles. They constitute a solid theoretical
framework for an approach to optimization of input-
output processes. They lead to the identification
of a least-cost combination of inputs, and a rate of
input, given the prices per unit of inputs and a
price per unit of output, that maximizes net benefit.
But, optima cannot be established from general
principles alone. It is absolutely necessary to

quantify the relationships--to establish how much output per unit of labor, for a given combination of equipment and labor, and so on.

It is, therefore, on the establishment of quantified physical relationships that the whole art or science of costing rests. This is as true for systems whose output is national defense, social welfare, reduced air or water pollution, as it is for a farm or factory. The first task of cost analysis, therefore, is an empirica investigation of technological relationships.

Of course, since the end object of the analysis is optimization, this analysis will ignore technologically inefficient ways of using combinations of resources. The production surface of Figure 2C describes only technologically efficient ways of combining inputs to produce outputs. If some inept manager lacks the talent to produce as much output with specified machinery-labor resources as could be produced, his experience is ignored as not relevant to a substitutability curve.

Thus, given a technologically derived production function which identifies a large number of technologically efficient input combinations, after taking account of relative prices of inputs, the least-cost input-output relationship is restricted to the much smaller subset of input combinations which will be least-cost for some particular level of output. If these are arrayed according to level of output, a single optimized cost function is established which describes cost of technologically efficient and least-cost ways of producing output, as a function of output. This lies on the points of tangency in Figure 3B.

It is the cost function that is developed in this way that is relevant to an optimizing cost-benefit analysis. If input prices change, this function will change, not merely because more or less is paid for inputs, but because the least-cost ratio of various inputs will lie differently on the technological production surface.

The kind of adjustment that is called for when input prices change may not, however, be easily, or quickly made. After a system has been constructed,

FIGURE 3

The Relevance of Relative Input Prices to
Proportion in Which Inputs are Used

A.

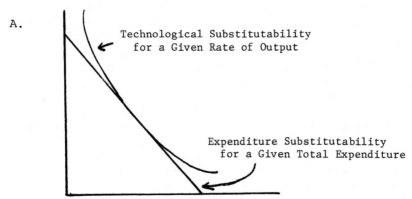

Technological Substitutability
for a Given Rate of Output

Expenditure Substitutability
for a Given Total Expenditure

B.

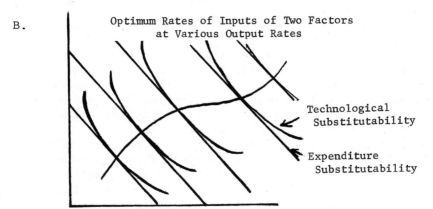

Optimum Rates of Inputs of Two Factors
at Various Output Rates

Technological
Substitutability

Expenditure
Substitutability

C.

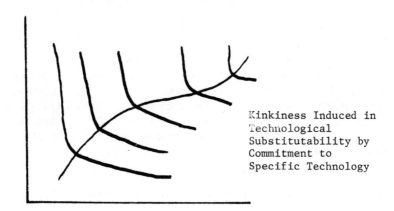

Kinkiness Induced in
Technological
Substitutability by
Commitment to
Specific Technology

it becomes technically more rigid: Some of the
flexibility of input substitution that was open to
the system designer is lost. For example, the
explicit physical form of an electric power vs. labor
substitution may be a choice between motor-driven
conveyor belts and hand trucks. Once the choice has
been made, the technical substitution is constrained,
and is "kinky" at the point chosen. The ratio of
inputs may not be much changed even if, the relative
prices of inputs change drastically. Obviously, the
system owner will wish he had foreseen relative price
movements. Further, when the equipment wears out,
and he has the opportunity to make a new system
design decision, he will choose one reflecting the
new relative price structure of inputs.

PROBLEMS IN COSTING

Whatever analytical sophistication has been
brought to cost estimating by modern accounting,
economic, statistical, or engineering analysis, cost
estimates have long been made, more or less successfully, by ill-educated men using simple and straightforward methods. The builder of a house or the planner
of a family vacation can estimate the cost if in the
first instance, he is able to identify the resources
involved, to estimate the price paid and quantity
used of each. Cost estimates can be made of efficient
and inefficient technologies if all resources are
counted, and the least-cost design thereby identified.

Of first importance in cost analysis is, then,
completeness. In attempting to be complete, certain
inputs are bound to be encountered which are used
but do not involve outlays. For example, suppose a
family has purchased an automobile for daily use.
Once purchased, costs are incurred regardless of the
rate of use, including the loss of value associated
with aging of the car (which goes on irrespective of
wear), insurance, garaging, etc.

The Use Rate of Fixed Investment

The principal component of fixed costs is the
charge made for physical property--rent, depreciation,

or some bookkeeping convention. That portion of
fixed costs which is relevant to decision-making
is the opportunity-cost portion--the value in some
other use, perhaps only a scrap value. An interest
rate applied to a scrap value. An interest
rate applied to a scrap value is a true opportunity
cost of maintaining a system in being.

   Costs incurred whether or not the family used
the car for a vacation would not be part of the
costs of a vacation, unless the family would have
bought a smaller car if it had not intended to vacation by car. To decide what part of costs of the
car are vacation costs, the family cost analyst
would have to decide what the most rational car
purchase would have been with and without vacation
plans and assign the additional costs to the vacations that the family would take in the car. He
must, of course, transform this into a rate by
dividing it into the total number of weeks of vacations during the lifetime of the car--a point that
would be highly conjectural for most families.

   Cost allocation difficulties also arise when
equipment--or labor--is used for several outputs
simultaneously. This occurs when railroad trackage
is used for passenger and freight service, raising
the question of what part of the cost of maintaining
the track should be charged against each service.
The marginality principle immediately suggests charging
the increment of cost associated with each unit of
traffic. It is in the nature of multioutput productive
operations that assigning input costs according to
marginal increment of cost associated with every
incremental output would not add up to the total
input cost. Over time, the result is that the
marginal increment is too small to maintain the
capital plant as it wears out or becomes obsolescent.

Marginality vs. Administrative Allocation

   Suppose family living expense outlays were
$10,400 per year, and the vacation added an increment
of $520 for five family members, that during 20 days

of vacation, 4,000 miles were driven. One could say
that vacation expense was $26 per day, $104 per person,
or 13 cents per mile. While these figures should not
be used for decision-making, they may be useful in
allocating fair shares of the over-all expense.

Suppose one of the vacation party was the mother-
in-law, who spent five days, during which time 500
miles were driven, and in the interests of harmony
insisted on paying her fair share of the expense.
Her share might be taken as only the additional
expenses incurred by her presence--a few dollars for
food and a shared room. Alternatively, her expense
might be allocated by one of the above ratios.

The economist's criteria is that of marginality:
He would say that only the _extra_ costs of the additional member of the vacation party were relevant to
the decision as to whether that party should go. She
should go if the additional benefit exceeded the increment of cost. But perhaps, although meeting that criteria, her enjoyment was not as great as the charge
that might be arbitrarily allocated to her but would
not have been incurred whether she went or not. She
might choose not to go; an increment of _net_ benefit
would be lost, as incremental benefit exceeded incremental costs. In this way an administrative cost-
accounting rule would have thwarted rational decision-
making.

It is important to recognize, on the one hand
the relevance of marginality to decision-making, and,
on the other hand, the prevalence of administrative
costing rules. These rules serve useful purposes.
Unfortunately, if--year in and year out--every member
of the family contributed only the incremental cost
of an additional member of vacation parties, not
enough would be collected to cover the cost of the
car; hence, the inescapability of some cost-allocating
rule.

This dilemma is at the heart of many costing
difficulties. It is often at the heart of difficulties which regulatory agencies face in setting rates,
where they attempt to set rates that cover the cost

of the service. Accepted practices have grown up,
which have become firmly entrenched in accounting
practice, the decisions of regulatory agencies and
courts. They are, in a sense, formulas for the
distribution of net benefit, and the question of who
should enjoy what kind of benefit (how society's
income should be allocated transcends systems analysis).
Most available cost figures are generated in accordance
with them, and it is not always obvious how arbitrary
allocations have affected the data.

The distinction between accounting for cost allocation and accounting for marginal cost-based decision-
making must be kept clearly in mind, particularly when
considering how to use, in cost-effectiveness analysis,
data from accounting records, or generated in support
of regulatory procedures. Allocation rules are too
valuable to disappear, so this problem will remain.

QUANTIFYING COSTS

In systems analysis, cost estimates of a very
large number of system configurations are often
needed. While many configurations may be derived
from a common basis of information, to cost out all
of the resources used in a large family of system
configurations is expensive drudgery. Particularly
during preliminary systems analysis, it is useful
to have simple if approximate means of estimating
costs. The interest is not unique to systems analysts
and managers: Contractors for building construction,
who make many competitive bids, must keep down the
cost incurred in preparing bids while protecting
themselves from the possibility of too-low bids.

Rough estimates of cost help the analyst zero
in rather quickly on the system alternatives which
are worthy of more thorough attention. Estimating
costs can be kept down if estimates can be based on
relatively few design features, and much has been
learned along this line.

There will be particular problems in developing
estimating procedures for different phases of a
system program. Each of these activities has its own
particular cost attributes.

Research and Development Costs

Where the particular result being sought can
be thoroughly specified, the effort of scientists
and engineers is spoken of as development. Even
for a fairly clear-cut development project, cost
estimating is likely to be crude. The resources
needed to accomplish the work are estimated by the
engineering supervisor, based on his personal evaluation of the development task. To estimates of the
number of man-months of skilled labor of different
categories may be added charges for the use of major
research facilities such as computers. To these
"direct" costs is usually added an overhead rate
based on experience as to the ratio of direct to
overhead cost. This is an arbitrary assignment of
charges--it is not marginal costing--and may bear
little relationship to the actual utilization of
facilities in a development task.

Capital Equipment

There are two investment costing tasks. On the
one hand, the dollar outlay for the creation of
system capital goods--equipment, facilities, land--
must be estimated. On the other hand, the charges
for use of this capital per unit of use must be
estimated. It is this latter that produces the rate
of capital usage costs that are used in cost-benefit
decisions. Comparisons of the cost of labor, capital,
etc., must be expressed in comparable terms--that is,
as rates of use. How the initial expenditure on
capital goods is converted into a rate is a source
of much that is unsatisfactory in cost-benefit analysis.
Unfortunately, at no point in the life cycle of
system usage will one know exactly how much capital
is left, and consequently what portion has been
used up per unit of time or use.

The equipment and facilities of a new system
are generally the largest single item of expenditure
in a system's history. The costs of investment are,
therefore, a focal point for cost-estimating techniques.
The approaches used by most estimators take as a

starting point a rough general design, so that estimates can be tied to some reality. As with R&D,
although major inputs are explicitly identified and
costed, some portion may be lumped into an overhead
charge as a short cut that avoids a substantial
volume of minor detail.

It is in investment costs that the analysis of
trade-offs of alternative system configurations comes
to a head. Perhaps a distinction may be made usefully
between trade-offs: (a) among different types of
equipment, and (b) between equipment and labor. It
is this latter that is the common subject matter of
microeconomics. Textbook curves assume substitutability
of capital and labor in infinitely small steps, with
diminishing returns to each, so that a precise equating
of the rate of substitution at the margin to relative
prices is possible. In practice, the design may be
alterable only in fairly large steps--one machine,
two, etc.

The charge for the use of capital is depreciation,
which is a rate. Depreciation proceeds both as a
function of time and as a function of use. Depreciation from use is appropriately charged against use,
since it is a cost that would not otherwise be
incurred. Depreciation from time is a cost of use
only to the extent that it preempts some other use.

To establish at what rate capital investment
costs should be charged against use, alternative
ways of utilizing the system must be taken into
account. Perhaps usage can be shifted in time. In
France, where vacations are concentrated in August,
some effort has been made to spread out vacation
schedules so as to achieve a more effective utilization
of recreational facilities. If this were done, less
of total cost would be assigned to August vactions.
Staggering school vacations in the United States could
be treated comparably.

Operating Costs

Operating costs, from a systems analytical
point of view, include only the out-of-pocket costs

of system operations. It is not uncommon in a large system for these costs to decline per unit of output as the scale of operation is increased up to near capacity, and for diminishing returns to be experienced only when the system is pushed to produce a rate of output beyond its planned capacity.

Thus, cost per unit of output depends on level of operations and cost per unit will be above the predicted value whenever operating rate is below predicted value. While this happens with operating activities, the effect is even more pronounced with overhead activities. Overhead operations will often be overstaffed when output is low, as the way that they are organized accommodates high rates of operation, and tends to be somewhat inflexible.

Errors in estimating the rate of system use are common. Frequently the rate of use is dependent on the individual decisions of many users who can exercise a choice as to which portion of a system they use. It is particularly difficult, for example, to estimate how inter-city travelers will split--by their individual decisions--the demand for highway, rail, and air transportation, and this is in addition to the problem of estimating the demand for inter-city transportation by any means.

It is not particularly difficult to see how one would estimate the labor force requirements for a given level of operations, making use of regression analysis for analysis of operations for which there is a historical record, or by engineering estimation. Further, considerable methodology has evolved in industrial engineering for estimating of labor inputs for the operation of machinery or performance of routine functions. Work operations may be minutely described, the time for each element estimated (the unit of work is called a therblig). Alternatively, men may be observed as they go through work operations in a mock-up, or a series of mock-ups. This same methodology may be useful for estimating system operating cost.

Similarly, costs of materials incorporated into outputs can be estimated as a function of system

output by data analysis or engineering estimates.
Inputs, such as fuel, which are not specifically
incorporated into the outputs, may offer more scope
for trade-offs with other costs of operation.

Social Costs

A private organization will be interested
principally in the costs incurred by that organization.
From its point of view a cost shifted to some other
part is a cost reduction. For example, as trucking
companies are not directly responsible for the cost
of maintaining roadways, only highway taxes are a
cost of this part of the system from their point of
view, although railroads must bear directly the cost
of maintaining their rights of way.

From the point of view of national welfare,
however, costs that are merely shifted are not
avoided. This points to a fundamental difference
between costing in support of private and public
systems analysis. Comparisons of costs in systems
analysis which seek to identify a socially optimum
system should take as costs the value of all resources
used to achieve an output, regardless of where the
burden of those costs should fall. To be sure, rates
of taxation, fees, and subsidies should be designed--
so far as is possible--so that the sum of direct
private costs plus these transfer charges equals
social cost and in seeking private profit, the
maximum social benefit is also obtained. Not infrequently, there is technically no way to achieve
this result, and even where there is, there may be
political and social objections. A compromise with
the desire to optimize may be necessary, in the
interests of equity--a less than optimum system may
be considered a _fairer_ system.

Whatever the impediments to practical realization
of social optima, there is much to be said for the
body politic being fully aware of the implications
of settling for something else. If the systems
analyst sets this task for himself, he will need to
make estimates of the nonprivate or social costs of
various system configurations.

This need exists in the operation of public programs as well as systems in which cost-shifting is done by private parties. Public agencies not infrequently are motivated to modify their operations, so as to favor systems that minimize their out-of-pocket costs, even where this means shifting those costs to some other agency, or to the general public. Only if, for some reason, the other agency or the public could produce the result more cheaply, would there be no conflict with a broad definition of public interest.

An outstanding example, and a frequent one, is the operation of municipal dumps. Not infrequently, a city administrator, in the interests of holding down the costs of trash disposal, operates a dump where it will blight a neighborhood. The city government does not bear the cost of reduced property values, soiled clothing, deteriorated paint, stench, and rats. If these costs were taken into account, as they should be in cost-benefit calculations from a public point of view, relocation might appear more attractive.

Presumably, under typical circumstances, the cost of trash disposal would be raised, to be collected by taxation throughout the city. In a sense, the benefit of a relocation decision would be restricted principally to the vicinity of the dump, but the cost would be city-wide. Yet if the relocation decision were sound, the persons in the immediate neighborhood would experience an increase in benefit exceeding the cost.

It is often difficult to distinguish between social costs and social benefits. Basically a social cost refers to resources used, but used external to the system. In the above example, cleaning bills, since they refer to resources, are a social cost—except that if the chosen alternative is to go dirty, and live in sooty houses, the benefit of greater cleanliness is experienced. To some extent, the division may be arbitrary, without harm to the analysis if double counting is avoided. A rigidly correct analysis would count as social costs the difference in costs of maintaining the same level of cleanliness with and without the dump. Whatever the conceptual merits of this point, if an effort is made to calculate it, it may be found that equivalent cleanliness (or dirtiness) is a technical impossibility, and there is nothing to cost out.

But equivalent, if not identical, states of benefit may sometimes be compared. Cross-country telephone lines detract from landscapes. In a valid comparison of the cost of systems, everything else must be held constant. This would mean that the telephone installer would have to include the cost of concealing wires, or otherwise precisely compensating those whose view was obstructed by the presence of the wires. Indeed, he should be permitted to choose the least-cost way of providing adequate compensation, which might very well be a cash grant somewhat less than the cost of burying his wires. The size of the grant necessary to satisfy potential viewers would, therefore, be an indirect measure of the loss of benefit. As it is equivalent to a cost avoided by not holding benefits unchanged, it is also equivalent to the social cost.

EXISTING DATA AS A BASIS FOR COST ESTIMATES

Typically, a system consists of "something old-something new." The distinction is loaded with implications for the strategy of quantifying input-output relationships. Cost relationships for what is old may be found by observation. With luck, there may even be records to be drawn upon. One would hope to find, for example, that electrical power generating plants have records of fuel consumption and power output, that the rate of output had varied considerably from time to time, and that a regression analysis could describe the historical record.

When this is done, the fit is generally only approximate. Some part of the deviation from a fitted smooth curve may be errors in recording the data, but other parts may be due to unknown differences in the quality of fuel. Through regression

analysis much of the variation about the best-fitted
curve can be accounted for by introducing additional
variables into the input-output relationship. Some
of these may be introduced as being relevant to the
optimization process, and others merely to account
for variations that might otherwise distort the
input-output relationship of real interest.

In practice, relationships of this sort must
frequently be developed from a large number of sources.
Often it appears that some sources are technologically
more efficient than others. Under these circumstances,
to fit a regression to the data leads to an input-output
relationship that is descriptive of what is obtained
with an average level of managerial competence, not of
the best that can be obtained. Whether or not the
result should be used unmodified in an optimization
problem, is an open question. One might argue, on
the grounds that the system under consideration will
be managed by average people, that it is appropriate.
But if one believes that the system can be optimized,
that past mistakes and current ineptitude can be overcome, it may be decided to use a relationship descriptive only of the least-cost operations.

Regression Analysis as an Estimating Technique

Regression equations that relate the quantity
of inputs to specific design or operating attributes
are especially useful when another of a large class
of comparable equipment is under consideration. An
example is aircraft construction costs. From U. S.
Government records, an expression for estimating the
initial tooling costs of a new design can be derived
as a function of these characteristics. Airframe
weight, maximum speed, and combat radius, as well
as initial tooling cost, were obtained for seven
fighter and seven bomber aircraft. Scatter diagrams
showed no basis for separately estimating fighters
and bombers, and showed that no single factor could
provide satisfactory estimates of tooling cost.
Unfortunately, from a statistical point of view, if
various design factors are strongly associated with
each other, an indicated standard error looking
better than it should would result. Further, the

regression coefficients themselves would be biased.
Some estimate of the caution that should be exercised
in selecting variables for a regression can be
obtained from examination of the correlation matrix,
but this is not an exact method. The author of
this study chose not to use combat radius as well
as weight, although each had explanatory power,
because they were highly related to each other. The
regression he developed:

Tooling Cost (Million Dollars) = 43.04 + 2.069
(airframe weight
in 1,000's of
pounds) + .0495
(speed in knots)

explained 90.2 per cent of the variance in tooling
costs over a range from $8 million for a 7,000-pound
aircraft with maximum speed of 525 knots to $265
million for a 115 thousand-pound aircraft with a
speed of 550 knots. Estimates that would have been
made by the equation were within $22.1 million of
actual costs for about 9 of the 14 aircraft.

Such an equation might well be used on a first-
cut systems analysis, in which alternative aircraft
transportation systems were being considered. One
would hesitate, however, to accept or reject systems
where an error of $20-40 million in tooling costs
could affect the decision. Although finer analyses
are ultimately necessary, such estimating equations
can greatly reduce the number of analyses that must
be done in fine detail. More refined estimates must
be based on a more complete structuring of the problem.

Engineering Methods

Where the technological relationships sought
are of a nonexisting system--perhaps a new concept--
statistical methods lack the necessary data base.
Recourse must be made to the methods of engineering
which consist of creating a design and mode of
operation, estimating on the one hand the resources
needed to bring that design into being and on the

other hand the resources needed in its use. In such
an exercise, the system designer must make innumerable
technical choices depending on the range of alternatives by which a given result can be produced.
These are as full of detail as any elaborate structure;
review in your mind the number of variants that must
be open to the designer of a bridge, for example.
The inputs to produce a specific output, at various
rates of output, must be examined and a technological
input-output function developed. Indeed, several
will be developed and compared against each other.

AN EXAMPLE OF COST ESTIMATING IN SYSTEM ANALYSIS

Technological Basis of the Trade-off

The manner in which elements of the physical
design of a subsystem may be traded off against
each other to produce a minimum-cost design can be
illustrated by a radio communication link. The
principal elements of such a link are a transmitter,
a transmitting antenna, a communication path, a
receiving antenna, and a receiver. This is a
particularly convenient example, as in electrical
engineering relative power is expressed as 10 times
the logarithm (to the base of 10) of the ratio of
two power levels. Since the log of a ratio of 100
is 2, a 100-fold increase in power is called a 20-db
gain. If an antenna concentrates the radiation of
energy so that in the direction of concentration
it has been increased 100-fold, the antenna has a
20-db gain. A combination of a transmitter providing
20-db gain relative to a power of one watt plus a
20-db gain antenna gives a total gain of 40-db
relative to one watt since logs are additive. As 4
is the log of 10,000, it properly expresses the product of two multiplicative gains of 100 each.

Thus, the combination, known as effective
radiating power, can be obtained by a large number
of antenna gain-transmitter power combinations.
Any one can be examined to see if an extra db of
gain can be more cheaply obtained by increasing
antenna gain, or by increasing transmitter power.

Increasing receiver sensitivity, or improving the receiver antenna are other design alternatives that will in turn reduce the necessary effective radiated power, but for the moment, consider the transmitter-antenna subsystem alone, since the remainder of the system is in no way affected by the combination. To do this, we need cost functions:

(1) Relating relative transmitter power in db to cost;

(2) Relating antenna gain in db to cost.

Regression Estimating of Transmitter Costs

Two separate approaches to cost functions are illustrated by this example. The first, transmitter power, was obtained by a statistical regression on prices of transmitters obtained from the manufacturer's catalogues or military contract prices. As shown in Figure 4A the latter generally ran higher, reflecting the more rugged physical design of military hardware. By using a dummy variable for military or nonmilitary construction, all data can be used in a single regression. By regression analysis, a mathematical expression was obtained which was an unbiased approximation to the observations. This expression was of the form:

$$\text{Log } C = a + b \, P^{\propto} + c \, G + u$$

Where C is cost in thousands of dollars, a is a constant, b the increase in cost in dollars per decibel of power P, c the amount that must be added to the constant if cost of a militarized version G is wanted, and u is the standard deviation of that portion of cost not explained by P and G with an expected value of zero. Power is expressed as a ratio of db over one watt, abbreviated as dbw.

It is clear from the data that certain manu-facturers made available cheaper transmitters than were predicted by this expression. In rational cost optimizing it is these cheaper units--not average costs units--we would be interested in, unless there

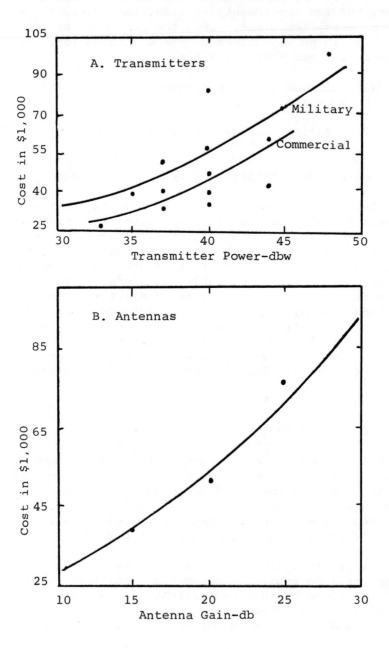

FIGURE 4

Cost of Transmitters and Antennas

is some factor relevant to the selection which is not
included in the estimating equation, as for example,
greater reliability in the more expensive units.
Unfortunately, we did not have reliability data for
the various transmitters, nor do we have any insight
into the design characteristics of transmitters of
various power levels.

To overcome the difficulty that regression
analysis does not provide costs of optimum design,
it might have been decided to have transmitter design
engineers design a series of transmitters say of 100,
250, 500, 1,000, 5,000, 10,000 watts power. From
these designs, bills of materials and contruction
manpower could be prepared and costed to yield a
relationship between cost and power. This is the
method of engineering synthesis. When a particular
power level was finally selected, the principal
design characteristics would already be known.

Engineering Synthesis of Antenna Costs

A synthesis generally is more work than a regression analysis, and is undertaken by a different type
of talent. To synthesize, one must have the ability
to complete hypothetical designs.

In the case of antennas, the launching efficiency
measured in db gain can be obtained by a wide range
of alternatives of two design features: the number
of wires in the antenna and the length of each wire.
Yet the laws of physics governing antennas do favor
particular combinations for a specific launching
efficiency. If antennas cost a certain amount per
foot of wire, the least-cost 20db gain antenna as
a function of the grid configuration will be identifiable at the bottom of a "U" shaped cost curve.
2 by 2, 3 by 3, 4 by 4, etc., configurations can be
used for an antenna with 20db gain, but--so long as
it is 20 db that is wanted--only the least-cost
design is of interest. The least-cost 22db antenna
will be identifiable at the bottom of another U, not
as cheap as the 20 db antenna, and of a different
physical design. Constructing the cost curve for a

whole family of efficiencies produces a family of U-
shaped curves, as is shown in Figure 5. Clearly,
only the designs represented by the lower boundaries
of this family are of interest. The envelope of
these curves summarizes the synthesis of many different
antenna designs.

Transmitter-Antenna Trade-off from Cost Functions

In a cost-trade, antenna and transmitters are
linear technical substitutes for a given effective
radiated power in db. This is shown in Figure 6.
The curvilinear family shows the combination of
antenna and transmitter that could be bought for 110,
120, 130 and 140 thousand dollars. Comparing the
two families of curves, one can easily see what it
will cost to obtain an effective radiating power of
60 db over one watt--the combination of 41 dbw
transmitter costing $56,000 and a 19 db antenna
costing $53,000 corresponds to the least-cost combi-
nation. It is apparent that the same result can also
be obtained at a higher cost by a different transmitter-
antenna combination. Further, an expansion path can
be constructed of least-cost combinations for any
effective radiating power.

The above demonstrates the manner in which--if
all possible physical combinations are explored--
the least-cost of what is physically feasible is
identified. In this case, all that the system
analyst need request of the antenna designer is
this envelope curve. He will select some antenna-
transmitter combination by use of this curve. Having
done so, he may inform the antenna designer that he
has selected an antenna with a gain of XXdb, costing
YY dollars. From his files, the antenna designer
extracts the technical information that what is
wanted is an xx by xx grid of wires zz long. If
the transmitter designer had synthesized designs,
he would go to his files. If costs had been
estimated from regression analysis, the systems
analyst would inform the transmitter designer that
he should design a transmitter with certain technical
features for a target cost obtained from the regression.

FIGURE 5

Cost of Antennas Achieving Various Gains (in db)

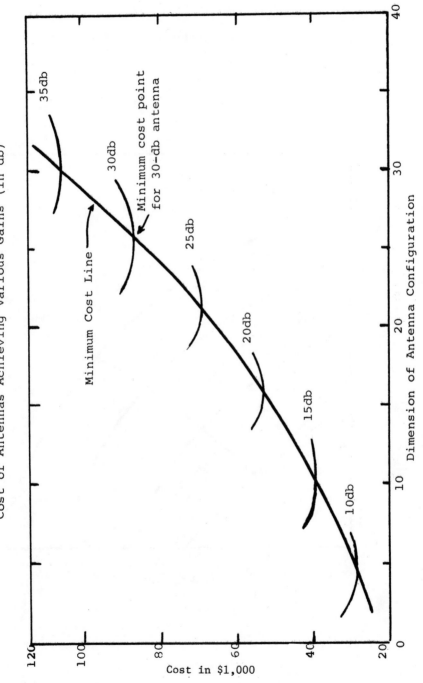

FIGURE 6

Cost and Technological Trade-offs,
Showing Least-Cost Combination for
Given Effective Radiating Power

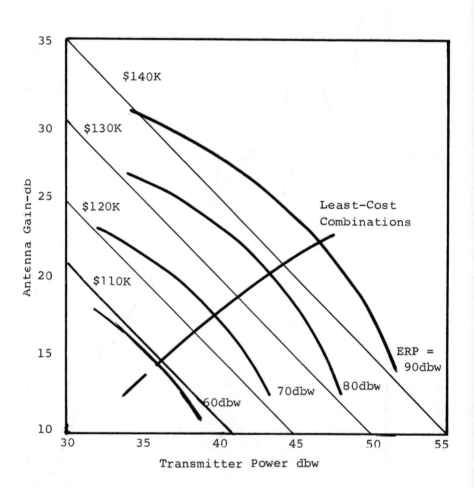

Parenthetically, the transmitter designer may have mixed views on such instructions, resenting the cost restriction before he has examined the design problem, but grateful that he did not have to work out a whole family of designs.

More Extensive Trade-offs

The system designer has taken a postulated effective radiated power of zz dbw (dbw is a reference level over one watt), for transmitter-antenna combinations, and priced them from the information he received from the antenna and transmitter designers.

In turn, the cost function of this combination would be traded in a comparable way against receiver sensitivity. A trade would be made between higher antenna towers, which have a lessened path loss, and reduced effective radiated power. Similarly, one high-capacity communication link might be traded off against several low-capacity links. Here, additional considerations would enter: for example, reliability. If, due to component failure, any one communication link would be inoperative 5 per cent of the time, two independent links with half the capacity of one might be preferred. (Strictly speaking, a valid cost comparison must be between configurations that perform comparably in all respects.) With two independent links there is _no_ communication only when both system A and system B are inoperative, which is .05 x .05 of the time, so that with two systems, there will be some communication 99.75 per cent of the time. This order of reliability might be achieved at a cost substantially greater than the cost of one system, but not double the costs because of operating and construction economies.

But full capacity may not be necessary at all times. The pattern of communication channel usage is irregular. Much of the time only part of capacity is in use, so many failures of _half_ circuits will be no inconvenience at all.

Ultimately, the systems approach to communications implies a trade-off between satellites, microwave

links, and wire systems. Here there are interesting
technical differences that affect cost of installation
and maintenance. Radio links jump from point to
point without necessitating acquisition of rights-
of-way, or construction of telephone line--either on
poles or underground. Maintenance is performed at
only a few points along a radio link communication
path, under generally more favorable working conditions.
On the other hand, radio spectrum space is a scarce
commodity that may be conserved by use of wired
communications. Satellites, with their broad geographic coverage, are particularly extravagant in
their use of the spectrum-geographic continuum.

The point of the above remarks is that cost
analysis cannot proceed independently of systems
analysis. Alternative configurations seldom if ever
produce fully equivalent results as did transmitters
and antennas. Even here, the equivalence was over-
stated; the reliability of transmitters is less than
that of antennas, and antennas are more subject to
wind damage.

CALCULATION OF SOCIAL COSTS

In his study of personal earnings and investment
in schooling (University of Chicago, August, 1965),
Giora Hanoch sought to estimate the internal rate
of return for various levels of schooling.[1] To do
this, it was necessary to estimate the cost to the
individual as well as the return from education.
Hanoch sought particularly to calculate the return
from an increment of education--that is of a high
school student who decides to complete high school
and so on. As income earned is a function of education, both his estimate of the cost of education
and the benefit from education were obtained from a
regression analysis that explained earnings as a
function of age, years of education, and other factors
such as sex, race, region of the country, family
background. For the years in which young persons
are educated, the regression gave an estimate of the
income foregone by going to school--a major element
in the cost of acquiring an education. The same

regression gave the time stream of income associated
with various degrees of education. By taking account
of sex, etc., Hanoch avoided attributing to education
differences in earnings that were really due to these
other factors; if education had been uniformly distributed over all of these groups, this technique would
not have been necessary. The basic work of the study
was, therefore, the multiple regression analysis on
the 51,000 persons available from the 1959 census
survey, using eighteen continuous and sixty dummy
variables by which the effects of differences in
earnings associated with mobility, marital status,
occupation, industry, and family characteristics
were separated from the earnings-education relationship.

     The rate of return implied by a ratio of cost
to future earnings is relevant to the decision each
June facing a student who might wish to know that
rate of interest, which, if used to discount the
difference between the stream of earnings with and
without the next step in his education, would exactly
equal the cost of obtaining that step. Thus, for
northern white males in grades nine-eleven, the income
foregone to complete the twelfth grade was calculated
to earn 16.9 per cent interest. For the northern
nonwhite it earned 30 per cent. Calculated this way
the results were not based on arbitrary rates of
discount of future returns, and the resulting information could be used by any person according to his
personal value judgment as to the time preference
of income.

     In the light of the high interest rates paid
for time purchases of consumer durables, undoubtedly
some would not be attracted by these rates of return.
From the standpoint of society as whole, however,
they are excellent, pointing to a social benefit
from education exceeding what some individuals find
attractive personally. Society has not filled this
gap by providing free education, to judge by Hanoch's
results.

COSTING AND SYSTEMS CONFIGURATION

Assume that a systems analysis has progressed to the point where a choice must be made among possible subsystem elements. The most efficient, least-cost way in which each subsystem may produce its output has been identified from studies of subsystem technology and relative prices of inputs. How rates of inputs as a function of least-cost output will vary is known.

At this stage, the task of systems analysis is principally to use these results in selecting a system configuration from the possible combinations of subsystems. Quite possibly alternative system configurations will bear little resemblance to each other--being composed of different subsystems or of subsystems interconnected in different ways; such a situation would preclude trade-offs of the possibility of increasing the rate of operation of one subsystem while decreasing the rate of another.

But not infrequently incremental trade-offs are possible. For example, passenger transportation in the northeastern United States can be performed by automobile, rail, and aircraft, and the proportions can be varied in fine degrees. Where such trade-offs are possible, the optimization of a system configuration will bear a marked resemblance to the optimization of a single subsystem input-output function. As was true with subsystem analysis, the inputs from substitutive subsystems can be varied so as to reach a point where the ratio of technical substitutability of these inputs is equal to the ratio of their prices.

One of the problems to be overcome in this approach will be establishing the prices of the inputs from various subsystems. As was noted in the earlier discussion, relative input prices play a role in identifying the least-cost technology. If these prices are not established correctly, a wrong technological choice will be indicated.

The impact that incorrect inter-subsystem transfer pricing might have can be illustrated by the

example of a large multidivisional integrated automobile company, in which each division corresponded
to a subsystem, operated by a division manager charged
with making a profit in his division. Products of the
foundry division, other material inputs, capital and
labor inputs, would be received by the engine division.
As a separate profit center, the engine division would
seek to balance off its inputs against each other to
seek the least-cost way of producing engines. If the
price of foundry products were arbitrarily set low,
the engine plant would find it relatively easy to
demonstrate an impressive profit, and would increase
the engine content of cars, while the foundry manager
would be hard pressed. The low price of foundry products would also lead the engine plant to use too many
castings relative to other inputs. This might take
the form of a wasteful attitude toward salvageable
but imperfect workmanship, for example.

How appropriate transfer prices can best be established depends on circumstances. If the products of a
foundry division can be compared with those of foundries
selling in open markets, there is a strong case for
using market prices. While this seems intuitively
obvious, there are indeed possible objections. Market
prices are not appropriate unless they are indeed the
prices which--as internal prices--would lead to a system optimum. A market price will satisfy this criteria
if it is the price that would be established in a perfect economic society of the neoclassical prescription--
one without restriction by monopoly, government regulation, or economic friction; where no buyer or producer
was individually able to affect the price of his product.
The exact degree to which actual market prices are affected by the failure to meet these conditions is not easy
to establish.

One of the resources is the capital plant, created
in the past, being used up over time at an undetermin-
able rate. The input cost usually assigned to capital
plant--depreciation--is an internal price established
by accounting conventions that deliberately overstate
the cost when plant is new--and understate it when it
is old. To say that "there are no capital costs in
flying a fully depreciated airplane" shows a misunder-
standing of the fact that--whatever the depreciation

history--so long as the airplane has a market value
and alternative uses, it costs something to use it.

The cost of any input should be considered as
what is foregone to obtain it. The resources used
by a system are costs in this sense when the inputs
could have been used for some other purpose, if not
employed on the system. Prices, as established in
a competitive economy, tend to be set according to
alternative opportunities for their use. Under these
circumstances, the outlay for inputs at market prices
may indicate the opportunity costs of the system to
society. Some prices will, however, reflect not alternative opportunities but the scarcity of an input with
no comparably valued alternative uses. A surge in
demand may temporarily result in an input price far
above the cost of reproducing those inputs, which is
the long-run opportunity cost. Also the inputs may
be unique, and not subject to duplication.

Any portion of price above duplication cost may
appropriately be excluded from a public oriented cost
estimate, especially in a system to be operated for
long periods. Technically this portion, known as
economic rent, is an outlay that represents no alternative opportunities foregone for resource use. There
are many examples, such as payments made to owners of
mineral deposits, unique labor skills, or franchises
granted by governments. As economic rent must be
paid, it is an out-of-pocket cost to a private system operator, and relevant to his system optimizing
decision although it leads to suboptimizing from
society's point of view. The collector of economic
rent may be able to obtain an inordinately large
share of the benefit of a system. This may be hard
to redress in systems operated for the public benefit.

Internal prices as established by administrative
fiat may also deviate from free market prices by lack-
ing flexibility of market prices. To some extent at
least, this difficulty can be reduced by arranging
transfer prices to change according to fluctuations
in marginal cost. This has been done with electric
power rate structures, by letting rates vary according to marginal costs at the time of day, season, or
peak load demand.

Government could clearly do a better job than it
does in establishing internal prices. Real property
is often transferred among agencies at zero cost, on
the grounds that the buildings and land are already
in hand. Admittedly, the monumental design of many
public buildings would result in singularly low rent-
als per square foot in the open market, but a zero
transfer price is clearly inappropriate and must lead
to excessive use of space.

COST, TIME, AND EXPERIENCE

Cost functions in analytical expressions, or cost
estimates may very well take account of expected
changes in costs and prices during the period of system construction and operation. Historically, prices
and wages move upward. Interest rates also change.
These movements affect the cost of procuring a system,
and cost of operation during its useful life. Price
trends are likely especially to affect operating costs,
as operation follows the actual procurement of the
system.

Reasonable assumptions as to future prices depend
considerably on the assumptions made about long-run
governmental policy toward inflation, wages, and interest rates. In the United States, under 2 per cent per
year increase in the GNP price deflator (the most
general of all indicators of price movement) is accepted without qualm. Above that is denounced as inflationary. In many countries, particularly underdeveloped
countries, inflationary experience far exceeds the U.S.
pattern, and can only be estimated as part of a general
political assessment. Wages can be expected to increase
in the U.S. by at least the long-run productivity trend
of 3.2 per cent per year. No long-range upward trend
can be projected for interest rates. The prime interest rate--the rate undiluted by risk--is very much the
creature of the central monetary authority. Historically and geographically, very high interest rates
characterize low states of economic development.
Interest rates paid by governments, though low, move
with the general rate. A rate of about 4 per cent is
a reasonable assumption for long-run projects. State

and local government rates are affected by tax advantages, and do not reflect social costs in the same
way as interest without this advantage.

Further, the efficiency with which a system con-
verts inputs to outputs may show a long-run upward
trend. In the United States, the long-run productivity trend has been about 3.2 per cent per year. But
this is the result of a complex mix of structural and
other changes in society--movement from low to high
productivity industry, replacement of old techniques
of performing such basic functions as transportation
with new types of systems, and improvements in the
efficiency with which any one system is operated.

In what sense may the productivity expectations
associated with a system proposal under study be
atypical? First, in any area to which the system
approach is applied, a substantially above average
technological change must be expected at the time of
installation, accompanied by a commensurate productivity increase. This effect is expected in the cost-
benefit analysis that supported adoption of the system. The second consideration is the prospect for
further technological change. This too should be a
factor in system analysis.

It might be supposed that the installation of
the new system concept would have exhausted the
opportunities for further technological change, or
at least preconditioned system operators against them.
Typically, however, the phenomena of learning and
familiarization with new systems has produced further
operating efficiency over time. The practical results
of learning have been summarized by the expression:

$$Y = ax^b$$

where Y is average direct man-hours per unit of output, and b is a value less than unity, so that Y
declines as x, the cumulative output, increases.

The "system" for which learning has been studied
most is airplane factories. A summary in the form
of a progress or experience curve, linear on double

log paper, fits most empirical data. A certain
percentage reduction in cost for every doubling of
cumulative quantity produced is indicated by such a
curve--in short, if the second output of an operating
system cost 85 per cent of the first, the fourth should
cost 85 per cent of the second, and so on. It is not
possible to state, a priori, what the learning curve
parameters of a new system will be, though early experience in the operation of a system might be used to
predict later results.

CONCLUSION

Cost analysis in the first place is based on the
physical relationship by which inputs are transformed
to outputs. To understand cost functions, these processes must be examined. There are certain general
principles, mainly related to changing ratios of input
usage that result in diminishing returns but perhaps
constant returns to scale. The multiplicity of inputs
is a fundamental concept. However, continuous varia-
bility of ratios is not, despite the smooth curves so
often used in textbooks. For discontinuous relationships different analytical techniques are used.

Relative input prices, given a pattern of physical
relationships, lead to some least-cost way of obtaining
any specified output. To find that is part of the system costing problem. It is not constructive merely to
enumerate costs without the certainty that the least
cost means of obtaining specified benefits is being
costed.

Inputs are in some cases investment goods, used
over time. There are many problems associated with
allocating over time.

Most costs of inputs are set to allocate total
cost, so that they will be covered, regardless of the
form of physical input-output relationships. The
resulting cost data are generally not relevant to
optimizing decision-making.

NOTE TO CHAPTER 5

[1]Giora Hanoch, "Personal Earnings and Investment in Schooling" (unpublished Ph.D. dissertation,
University of Chicago, 1965).

CHAPTER **6** OPTIMIZATION

The objective sought with a system is either:
(a) to obtain a given result or combination of results
at least cost, or (b) the maximum possible results
from available resources. Because resources sufficient
for all purposes are never available, they must be
allocated--in other words, _economized_. Either of the
above amounts to maximizing _net_ benefit, which is the
value of output less the cost of inputs expressed in
comparable terms, obtained by choosing the level of
output and the pattern of inputs which produces that
maximum, subject to a resource or output constraint.
Thus, cost or input functions and benefit or output
functions are steps on the road to the selection of
optimum system configuration and level of outputs.
The nub of optimization is the technique of using
cost and benefit functions jointly to identify the
configuration and mode of operation that most fully
satisfy what are understood to be the ends sought.

An optimum can be determined either: (a) by an analytical technique that precisely identifies from functional
relationships to some "peak" of net benefit as each
factor subject to control is changed; or (b) by a
search--perhaps systematic and perhaps not-- among
possible outcomes for one that is best. Search is
surely the first procedure historically. Later sup-
planted by analytical techniques, search has recently
taken the sophisticated form of linear programming,
and analytical techniques have gone far beyond calculus.

OPTIMIZATION OF SYSTEM OPERATION
VERSUS SYSTEM CONFIGURATION

Systems analysis is usually directed at optimization of configuration--picking and choosing among

89

the possible variations of system hardware that can
be operated to produce the best result. Optimum
operation of a system in being is faced continuously
by all managers of existing, complex activities. The
configuration problem is to consider the differences
in optima that could be achieved by managers, each
locked into a specific system configuration, as the
details of that configuration were changed. Looked
at before a commitment is finally made to a specific
configuration, this question is intensely interesting.

It is one thing to examine the results that could
be achieved by a mixed bag of managers ranging from
inept to brilliant, and another thing to assume a
faultless manager. It would appear to be the path
of consistency in an optimizing analysis, to show
what could be achieved. A more cynical view would
be that as the average manager is, after all, only
average, only a mediocre technological result should
be expected from him, and any estimate should be of
what can be expected of such a person. Which option
is chosen is a matter of taste.

In the most limited sense, an optimum is some
maximum value--a race car adjusted for the greatest
possible speed. Where output is describable by a
continuous mathematical function, the optimum is the
point of an extreme value for which the quantity of
all inputs is thereby identified by the first derivative. In graphic terms, it is simply the point where
an input-output function is parallel to the input axis.
Where there are several input variables, partial derivatives, all equal to zero, establish this point. As
some functions may have several localized extreme
values of maxima or minima, additional tests are
needed to confirm that an extreme value is a maximum.
Minima are distinguished from maxima by the second
derivative, which distinguishes the direction in which
the function is curving.

The relative simplicity and widespread understanding of the techniques of calculus provide an incentive
for expressing input-output functions in mathematical
relationships to which differential calculus can be
applied directly. The mathematically necessary

assumption of a continuous relationship is often only
a modest deviation from reality: For an indicated
optimum of 1.33 man-hours, one or two man-hours will
be close to optimum. Taking the nearest integer values
as the optimum is usually acceptable.

It is at the stage of optimization that direct
comparisons must be made between input and output
functions. If care was not taken to express them in
common terms, this comparison cannot be made. Outputs
and inputs must be expressed as functions of rate of
operation of a system--rate being the common element
that makes it possible to combine them into a single
expression. For example, if an engine were to be
tuned for maximum energy per gallon of fuel, an output function expressing energy as a function of RPM,
and an input function expressing fuel consumption as
a function of RPM would be used. Commonality must be
retained throughout the whole range of costs and benefits that are to be compared. The common measure
usually chosen for inputs and outputs is the price
per unit. It will be clear why analysts so often
seek to use dollars as the common measure. It is
very natural to measure inputs in dollar prices--
particularly as in complex optimizing problems, comparisons must be made among many kinds of inputs.
Hence, it is also expedient to measure benefits in
dollars so that inputs and outputs can be compared
directly.

Optimizing Operation of a
Specific System Configuration

There is a fine line between costing and optimization. Cost analysis is not merely the estimation
of costs of a specified bill of particulars, for the
mix of inputs must be chosen according to prices of
the various possible inputs, and the technical trade-
offs among them.

Among the first of the trade-offs to be made in
a process of optimization are trade-offs among inputs.
This has been described in the preceding chapter as
part of the development of a cost function. A cost

function that describes only technologically optimized combinations of inputs in those proportions that are least cost, given relative factor prices, must be obtained.

Substitutability is more characteristic of some classes of inputs than others. Materials incorporated into output are often quite rigidly related to the quantity of output. Labor and capital are often more easily substituted for each other, or for such inputs as electric power. Substitution of capital for labor is the essence of decisions to expand system equipment in the interest of reducing operating requirements for labor. Such a choice is increasingly attractive as wages increase relative to the cost of equipment, or as equipment improves technologically. Research and development directed at system process improvement tends to favor capital intensity.

An optimum mix of all inputs, when some of the inputs are very durable can, in fact, be only one of those things that in the words of Gilbert and Sullivan, "we shall achieve in time." It is achieved when no shift in the ratio of inputs to each other would produce a given output more cheaply, and when no greater profit could be made by either expanding or contracting production. Quite likely, this state is seldom attained in real life, but it is still useful as a criterion for optimization.

For any given quantity of output, there is a mix of inputs that will produce it at least cost. This mix can be established by equating (1) the technological substitutability among inputs--a ratio of the extra quantity of input A needed to maintain rate of output in the face of a reduction in input B and (2) the ratio of relative prices of these inputs. If there are many inputs, the ratios for every possible pair must be equal. If this were not so, it would be possible to change the input combination in favor of those that at the margin cost less than the added revenue from the technical result that could be obtained by purchasing them with the money released by not buying other inputs.

This point could be established for a whole
range of output levels. For each of these, the combined cost of all inputs would be known, and these
costs as a function of output level would yield cost
as a function of output restricted to technically
efficient combinations that were also least cost.
This cost function may be thought of as a first-stage
suboptimization.

The above discussion of optimization is, in fact,
a very limited one. It has passed over many special
conditions, some by no means rare, where the rules
for cost maximization indicate special types of
behavior. Monopolies, or firms with some bargaining
power vis-à-vis inputs (e.g., wages) are important
special cases.

COST-BENEFIT COMPARISONS

The essence of optimization is the cost-benefit
comparison. This must not be a simple ratio of averages, but must be the ratio of an increment of cost
from increasing the operating rate of a system or
investment in it and the corresponding increment of
benefit. Suppose all costs and all benefits have
been combined into a single function. Benefit and
cost both increase as a function of rate of output
but not necessarily linearly or in the same proportion.
Changes in net benefit depend on relative rates of
change of benefit and cost as functions of rate of
output. As Figure 7 shows in a graphic representation,
the point where benefit and cost functions are parallel
is the point of maximum separation, and mathematically
is the rate of output for which the first derivatives
are equal. The objective of maximizing net benefit,
as expressed by the relationship:

Net Benefit = Total Benefit - Total Costs

is achieved for continuous functions by differentia-
ting the functions, setting the derivative of net
benefit equal to zero so that at the optimum:

$$\frac{d\ (Total\ Benefit)}{d\ (Rate)} = \frac{d\ (Total\ Cost)}{d\ (Rate)}$$

FIGURE 7

Optimization with Linear Benefits
and Curvilinear Cost Functions

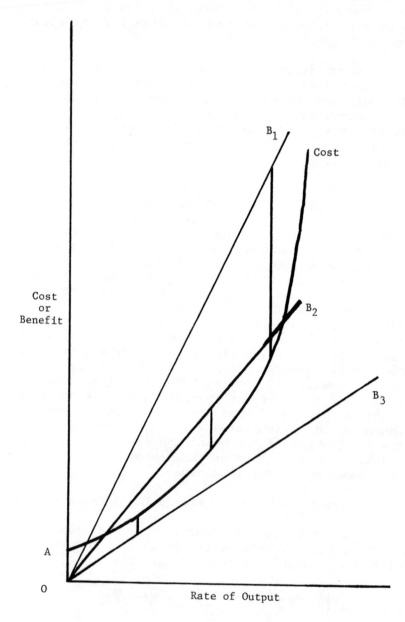

Cost
or
Benefit

B_1

Cost

B_2

B_3

A

0

Rate of Output

It is <u>not</u>, however, the point where benefit-cost
ratio is greatest. It will be seen that to take the
maximum ratio (the point at which lines drawn from
the origin tangent to the cost and benefit curves
would have the greatest angular separation) as the
optimum would result in less <u>net</u> benefit (and a lesser
vertical distance between the benefit and the cost
function) and less output.

It will also be seen that even without changing
the cost curve, the optimum output rate is changed if
the benefit per unit of output is changed. B_2, for
example, represents the lower optimum that results
with a benefit function whose lower slope denotes a
lesser benefit per unit of output.

Note further, that even if cost exceeds benefit
at all levels of output--as it might with a politically
inspired water system--there is still an optimum rate
of operation. Cost-B_3 illustrates net loss from
operating a system whose benefit is described by B_3.
This will be less than if the system were shut down
(because the cost-B_3 vertical separation at the point
of parallelism is less than OA).

OPTIMIZATION AND LINEAR FUNCTIONS

The curvature of benefit and cost functions is
critical in optimization. Suppose, for example, that
both were straight lines, and the benefit function
was steeper than the cost function. Net benefit would
increase with every increase in the rate of operation.
If, on the other hand, the cost function was steeper
than the benefit function, the system should not be
operated at all, as <u>any</u> operation would result in less
net benefit than no operation.

Because life is not like this, we know instinctively that linear cost and benefit functions are
nonsense. Typically, as rate of operation increases
it takes more inputs to get an extra unit of output,
which can only be represented by a cost function that
becomes steeper and steeper as output increases, or
the increment of benefits from an extra unit of output

decreases, with rate of operation. Only curvature in
the cost or benefit function will result in there being
a point of parallelism between gross benefit and gross
cost, and hence a point where vertical separation
between the two is greatest.

The mechanics of optimization is the principle
reason why it is important, in deriving cost and benefit functions, to avoid linear approximations. The
linearity underlying cost functions may not be recognized: If average cost per unit of output declines
curvilinearly from 6 dollars for one output to 4 for
two, and 3-1/3 for three, it expresses the linear cost
relationship, Cost = 4 + 2 times number of inputs.

The principal reason why linear functions are
used is the quality and quantity of available data--
not to mention the disturbing effects of phenomena not
explicitly taken into account in cost or benefit
models--are such that from a statistical point of view,
curvilinear functions are not justified. If a quadratic
or exponential function is fitted to data, but the
approximation is mediocre, the curvature and the points
of inflection are highly undependable--and, of course,
the point identified as the optimum depends precisely
on them.

Where cost and benefit estimates are very approximate, these characteristic problems serve, to an extent,
to justify the use of cost-benefit ratios. If the ratio:

$$\text{Cost-benefit ratio} = \frac{\dfrac{\text{Benefit}}{\text{Rate of Output}}}{\dfrac{\text{Cost}}{\text{Rate of Output}}}$$

is greater than one, and each function is linear, it
is certain that operation of the system at some rate
is justified; otherwise not. The logical conclusion
that follows from such a ratio is that the system
should be operated at the highest possible rate--
which is determined where some one input is completely
exhausted, where capacity is reached, or where other
uses of resources cannot be avoided. If cost-benefit
ratios of various systems are compared, it is clear

that the system with the highest ratio should be
operated at capacity before any resources are devoted
to the next best.

Such practices, of course, do not correspond
either to usual decisions, or intuitive rationality.
The administrator substitutes his own judgment as to
optimum point where the analysis fails to guide him--
and this cannot be quarreled with so long as administrators have an insight into cost and benefit functions
that statisticians and analysts are not able to dupli-
cate, so long as they operate with the restriction that
they will use only information available in numerical
form.

OPTIMIZATION WHERE RESOURCES ARE ABSOLUTELY LIMITED AND FUNCTIONS ARE LINEAR

Where benefit and cost are linear functions, an
optimum exists where there is some absolute limit to
how much of some input may be available--which, when
exhausted, defines the optimum. Such a limit may be
only an optimum in the short run, until new machines
are added, whereon a new optimum is established,
corresponding to the new capacity.

If benefit is linearly related to several inputs
which are limited in supply, one may be exhausted
before the others, so that at maximum benefit some
input will be completely used, while the others are
still unused. Naturally, a rational input allocation
would call for some use for the excess. They can be
used only in combination with other inputs, and indeed
to use this "excess" may require diverting to a new use
some of the inputs that were otherwise completely used
up. If, in a second system, the ratio of the "excess"
inputs to the inputs fully-used for the first system,
and the benefit from the second system relative to the
first is large enough, the allocator will gain by making
such a diversion in the interests of fuller utilization
of all inputs under his control. Situations of this
general sort can be approached by the methods of linear
programming.

A business example, where the "benefit" is a mix of radios and TV sets, will illustrate the point. Suppose that the available inputs relate to outputs linearly as follows:

    1 TV set = 1 picture tube + 10 small tubes
                     + 100 resistors + 10 man-hours
               of labor

    1 radio set = 6 small tubes + 30 resistors
                      + 2 man-hours of labor

A manufacturer can, from such equations and the prices of radio and TV sets, figure out how many of each to produce from an inventory of parts and with a given labor force, so as to yield a maximum profit. If he had not yet acquired these inputs, he would need to take into account relative input prices. As all economic results--and any transformations achieved by a system or subsystem--are achieved by combination of several inputs, and linear programming deals particularly with problems in which several types of resources can be used to produce several types of outputs, linear programming is highly compatible with economic rationale.

Linear programming resolves with great effectiveness allocation problems where there is a wide variety of input-output combinations that can be reasonably well represented as linear. It can be used effectively, for example, for factories which have many machines-- some perhaps identical--for which output on any one machine is a linear function of labor and material, but the machine has an absolute capacity constraint. Suppose a vast hospital system comprising dozens of hospitals had obtained linear estimates of patient- days of care in each of its hospitals and the functions differed because of physical layout, etc. Further, certain resources such as beds or staff were absolutely limited. Linear programming would be useful to arrive at patient and staff allocations.

While inflexible in certain ways, linear programming is highly flexible in others. It is possible, for example, to specify minimum outputs of some or all benefits. By giving very direct evidence as to

which input limitations, if removed, would most improve
benefits, linear programming can give useful guidance
as to how additional funds might be most effectively
used--or where budgets might be cut with the least
unfavorable effect on benefits. It might also pin-
point surplus resources.

OPTIMIZATION IN THE FACE OF UNCERTAINTY

Both linear programming and continuous function
models are couched in the language of deterministic
mathematical relationships. There is, to be sure,
some uncertainty as to the accuracy of function parameters, but optimization takes the best-guess values
and proceeds as if they were gospel. This flaw may
be mitigated by sensitivity analysis--in which parameters are varied over a range to which statistical
measures of significance may give some clue.

But there is a more significant uncertainty
problem: Frequently, the output that will result
from a given combination of inputs is really a chance
event. There may even be several possible outcomes
of an input process that are so distinctly different
that it is meaningless to represent them as variations
about an average value.

Statistical decision theory has provided techniques for identifying optimum decisions in uncertain
situations, once a specific decision has been made as
to the degree of uncertainty attached to various outcomes. As such, it provides a basis for tracing through
the implications of various courses of action, and
selecting a best or optimum strategy.

Suppose informed judgment held that there was a
4 per cent chance that a survey of the ocean floor
might discover a sunken treasure ship known to carry
gold worth $40 million. The cost of the survey would
be $1 million, so that if the survey were successful,
the net benefit would be $39 million, and, if unsuccess-
ful, the surveying party would be $1 million in the
hole. If a decision were made <u>not</u> to carry out the
search, there would be no change in benefit. Thus,

there are four possible situations, with the following effects on net benefits:

	Treasure Found(.04)	Not Found(.96)
Search conducted	40-1=39	0-1= -1
No search	0	0

The _expected_ value of conducting the search is:

$$[39\ (.04) + -1\ (.96)] = .600$$

which, being positive and in excess of the expected
value of no search, would indicate the search to be
a good investment with an expected return of sixty
cents on the dollar. It is quite possible to consider
a number of search programs. Perhaps a less ambitious
search costing only $300 thousand was judged to have
a 2 per cent probability of success. Then:

$$(40.0 - 0.3)(.02) + (-0.3)(.98) = .500$$

which yields a lower expected value, although risking
a lesser amount. These examples suggest a diminishing return to search activity. Venturing an additional
$700 thousand has an extra payoff of $100 thousand
From a broader range of search programs a continuous
function between input and expected output could be
constructed. The method can thus be used to identify
an optimum search strategy, taking into account the
dollar value placed on avoidance of risk.

OPTIMIZATION OF STRATEGIES

    Uncertainty may not stem from the environment,
but from the response of other persons. Taking account
of how response is affected by system characteristics
is a desirable refinement in systems analysis. For
example, the rules governing tax exemptions are carefully researched by taxpayers and their advisers, and
the Internal Revenue Service (IRS) must necessarily
take account of the results of such searches, and the
strategies open to taxpayers. That such behavior can

be treated by game theory was elaborated in 1944 by
John von Neumann and Oskar Morgenstern in their
classic, <u>Theory of Games and Economic Behavior</u>.[1]

Game theory is well developed for situations
that fulfill rather restrictive mathematical considerations. These limit the application of game theory
in its present state of development. It is necessary,
for example, to detail the entire spectrum of possible
moves and strategies for all players.

A constraint in most of game theory is that the
game must assume only a transfer of benefits between
players, without additional benefits created or destroyed
by the cooperative or destructive acts of the players.
This condition would be approximated if Treasury rules
affected the division of taxpayer income between the
Treasury and the taxpayers without affecting the total
amount of such income. While this restraint serves to
limit game theory, it is a difficulty that can be overcome by creating a dummy player, whose benefit varies
to make the game a zero sum one.

Game theory not infrequently identifies the best
strategy as being a "mixed" strategy, wherein the
action taken by the first player may be randomly
selected from several, so that the second player will
not be able to predict the first move. For example,
strategies for the IRS might be: (1) to audit all
returns, (2) not to audit any returns, and (3) conduct
a sampling audit. If all returns were audited, the
net payoff to the Treasury would be reduced by heavy
auditing costs; given only partial auditing--and a
sufficient penalty for cheating--the taxpayer's best
strategy with partial audit may be to be as honest
as with a 100 per cent audit. On the other hand, if
audits were sufficiently rare or the penalty low
enough, the taxpayer's best strategy would be to cheat.
The models of game theory identify the best strategy
for each unequivocably, given the assumptions.

That game theory requires a listing of all possible strategies and responses, may be a serious limita-
tion to its use. To think out strategies may be a
great deal of work. Game theory gives little guidance

as to how possible strategies might be discovered, or
how the payoff from each might be calculated. These
conditions must be specified before the theory is
applied, and only the best of specified strategies
is indicated as optimum.

To use game theory, considerable data must be
obtained from real life, as with other optimizing
techniques, and the validity of the results depends
on the quality of the data and the completeness with
which possible strategies and responses are searched
out.

Gaming

Game theory must not be confused with gaming.
The latter is a technique in which individuals take
the part of players in an artificially created game,
designed to correspond to a situation of interest.
Gaming can be used as a means for creating data, or
for uncovering strategies that would not occur to
an analyst. Beyond this, games can serve to obviate
the need for explicit models, as the players can perform the function of the model, perhaps reacting in
ways that could not be expressed in models.

OPTIMIZATION OVER TIME

Future benefits and costs are worth less than
present ones. This point is incorporated into cost-
benefit analysis by comparing present values of future
streams of costs and benefits from alternatives. As
noted earlier, there is neither a fully satisfactory
basis for selecting discount rates, nor any necessity
that costs and benefits be discounted at the same
rate, nor that the rate be at all future times the
same. The essential arbitrariness of _any_ discount
rate may sometimes make elaboration and refinement
somewhat meaningless. The difficulty with discounting, of course, undermines in part the whole concept
of cost-benefit analysis and optimization. Fortunately,
optima are often not particularly sensitive to discount
rates.

Table 1 is a hypothetical example of how discounting establishes net benefit of a system with a five-year cycle. It costs $200 to build, spread over two years, and starts to yield benefits in the second year. In the last year, it becomes expensive to operate and is sold for scrap value at the end of the year.

While discounting of future returns is routinely incorporated into analyses--using marginality or linear programming for estimation--it is less common to include, as part of the analysis, any consideration of how costs and benefits are affected by the dynamic response of a system over time. There is, in fact, a considerable gulf between static analysis and dynamic analysis, which is not bridged by discounting. While simplified assumptions can be made as to how benefits and costs are incurred at different periods and lagged or leading parameters can be estimated statistically, these techniques restrict dynamicism to rigid molds which may not be adequate to reveal disbenefits that may result from cyclical effects, or trends in costs, benefits, or rate of operation.

The methods of industrial dynamics are available to explore stability conditions of specific models, and the way they are affected by system parameters or subsystem components. Industrial dynamics is not, however, an optimizing technique, nor well integrated with microeconomics. It may be necessary to design a system by static analysis, and then analyze separately its dynamic properties. The possibility of dynamic instability is greater where there are time delays in the system, and there is feedback within the system or from output back to input. Unless there is some nonlinearity or constraint, it is possible to design a statically optimized system that will drive itself to destruction. Constraints are common in real life systems, but are sometimes overlooked in system models. Even systems that are stable in their usual environment may exhibit instability under the impact of an irregular flow of inputs, irregularity in the transformation functions (e.g., a machine breakdown), or in demand for output. A recent example is the failure of the Northeast power system. This large interconnected system seemed able to cope with a wide variety of

TABLE 1

HYPOTHETICAL COMPARISON OF COST AND BENEFIT
STREAMS DISCOUNTED AT 10 PER CENT (IN DOLLARS)

Year	Present Value of Dollar	Costs		Benefits			Contribution to Present Value
		Investment	Operating	Scrap	Gross	Net	
0	--	--	--	--	--	--	00
1	.90	100	0	0	0	-100	-90
2	.82	100	10	0	20	- 90	-74
3	.75	0	100	0	200	+100	+75
4	.68	0	100	0	200	+100	+68
5	.62	0	150	0	200	+ 50	+31
6	.56	--	--	75	75	+ 75	+42

Present Net Value of System Investment at Year Zero: 52
(Sum of Contributions to Present Value)

external and internal disturbances, until an accidental event uncovered a flaw in its armor. Often there
is no known way to analyze the reaction of a complex
system to all possible dynamic effects.

The simulation of experience with a system in a
dynamic environment is a possible approach to a dynamic analysis. Computerized simulation can, of course,
only explore the dynamic effects of whatever is incorporated in the computerized model. Simulations can
be run as games with real-life players, and a real-
life simulation may very well reveal some overlooked
aspect of dynamicism, which the analyst neglected to
put in his model.

SYSTEM-WIDE OPTIMIZATION

To optimize a system means to optimize the outputs
of a system as a whole relative to inputs to the system as a whole. This is done by selecting the configuration of subsystem black boxes from a larger
family of possibilities, specifying the basic characteristics of the boxes, and the level at which each
is to be operated.

A subsystem or "black box" of a system can be
described by a functional relationship between inputs
and outputs on the assumption that an optimum ratio
of inputs, given prices of inputs, and the most efficient technology, are employed. The levels of inputs
and outputs are, however, determined outside of the
system. In a sense, a demand is created for outputs,
and the black boxes of the system respond by demanding
inputs in turn. A sequence of demands flows back
from the output of the system as a whole through all
black boxes to appear as inputs to the system as a
whole.

In a simple case where all input-output functions
are linear, it would be possible to present all functions combined in the form of a matrix, each line
representing a subsystem, with coefficients for the
inputs and outputs. Some subsystems would absorb,
as inputs, the output of other subsystems. Through

mathematical manipulation, the system-wide outputs could then be expressed directly as a function of system-wide inputs. Because of the substantial inter-connections between boxes, the flow of one into another, and sometimes the feedback of output from one box into an antecedent box to create a circular flow, a system optimization must jointly and simul-taneously optimize every element of the system. At the point where system-wide analysis begins, however, much of the detailed examination of the technology that is entirely internal to subsystems should be complete, to be drawn upon by the systems analyst.

System optimization means defining these func-tions as including variations in the fixed hardware of the system. This hardware, of course, is what determines the investment cost of the system. Phy-sically, the possible alternatives are likely to take a number of specific and radically different forms. The use of trade-offs between types of system inputs may thus be even more restricted than in the analysis of subsystems. The system specification problem con-sists, therefore, principally of manipulating the level and the allocation among possible subsystems. Each time some exploratory change is considered, the level and mix of other inputs to achieve an optimum must be recalculated.

The level of benefits can be held fixed by increasing the benefit from one subsystem while decreasing the benefit from another. This is shown in Figure 8, where the benefit is defined as $B = aX + bY$, X and Y being particular kinds of benefits created by different parts of the system. The parts create bene-fits by using three inputs in various proportions. The input from "capital" is shown entering the bottom of each box to express the idea that it acts as a modifier of the way in which labor and materials are translated into benefits, although it should not be overlooked that capital is as much an input as labor and materials and contributes as fully to output.

Generally speaking, the optimization of a system--and the problems and pitfalls associated with it--are those found in the first instance in subsystem optimization

FIGURE 8

Transformation of Multiple Inputs into Multiple
Benefits by a System Composed of Two Subsystems

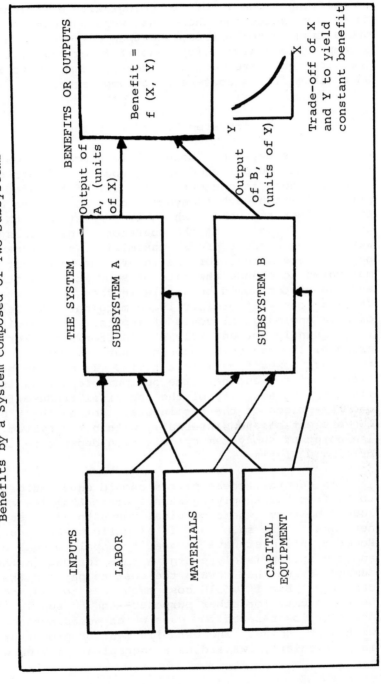

107

Indeed optimization was seen to proceed from initially identifying a family of technologically efficient cost functions, selecting those that were optimum for the prevailing factor prices, and then going on to perform a comparable analysis for benefit functions (for which the techniques are less well developed), and to identify an optimum from a cost-benefit comparison.

Intersystem Transfer Prices

For a subsystem, "benefit" is frequently an intermediate output used as an input by another subsystem. There is conceptually a set of transfer prices at which each subsystem could "sell" its output to other subsystems which is consistent with an optimum. In short, if the operator of each subsystem were an independent profit-maximizing entrepreneur, paying these prices for his inputs, he would not be motivated to change the rate of subsystem operation, and the system would be stable in rate of operation. These prices will ordinarily be marginal revenues of outputs and marginal costs of inputs. But marginality is frequently not entirely straightforward. For example, it frequently happens that the outputs of two black boxes flow into a third. If one can be traded off for another, the optimum proportion is fixed by the equality of the technical trade-off and the prices of the two inputs. But as their prices are established internally within the system, the point of subsystem optimization depends on the pricing analysis.

In general, these prices should equal marginal costs from the supplying subsystems. Examples are found, however, where marginal costs to all uses are not equal. One such case is electric power generation. Power plants must have a capacity equal to peak demand, and can appropriately charge a rate for use in the peak demand period that covers the cost to pay for that capacity But it would cost much less to use the off-peak capacity for other purposes--and to supply this power at lower rates for uses which would not compete with peak demand. The establishment of proper prices is particularly awkward as a conceptual problem where

their duration differs, so that some method of allocating them over time must be hit upon.

SPATIAL OPTIMIZATION

The resources used to create benefits as well
as the benefits themselves are distributed across the
face of the map. To bring resources together requires
transportation, itself an element of many systems and
a user of resources. One dimension of many system
problems is, therefore, the optimization of spatial
relationships.

The interaction between transportation and production costs frequently determines the location of
industrial activity. The exploitation of natural
resources depends on their accessibility to ultimate
consumers, and the geographic distribution of consumers
and producers itself reflects cost differences and
characteristics of the transportation system.

Spatial relationships are of frequent concern
in public problems. Regional economic development
may be greatly influenced by transportation: Perhaps
a systems analysis for the development of a depressed
region will make use of a transportation model.
National highway systems, criteria for Federal support
of state and urban transportation systems, can hardly
avoid questions of spatial distribution. A frequent
spatial optimization problem is determination of
numbers or locations of warehouses or administrative
centers needed to blanket the entire country. Such
optimization relies on somewhat special characteristics and bodies of analytical technique.

The essence of classical spatial economic theory
is simply presented. In Figure 9A, the cheaper source
for the uses of an item purchasable at the same price
in city X and city Y, to which transportation cost
has been added, is shown as a function of distance
from each city. That the slope of the line represents
the added cost per unit distance is easily seen, so
that city price plus transportation cost is represented at all points along the axis by the vertical
distance.

FIGURE 9

Spatial Price and Cost Patterns

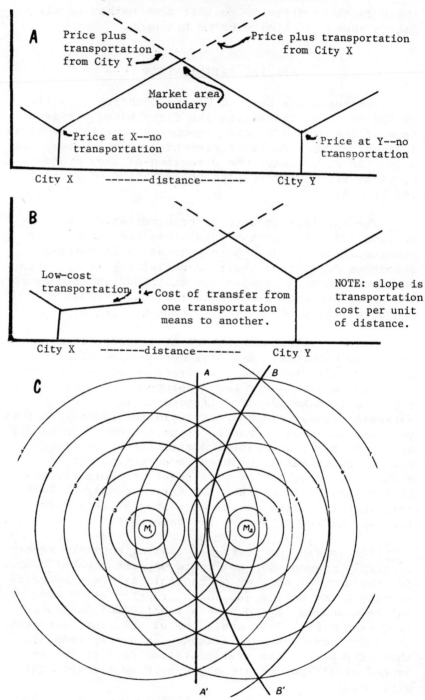

A

Price plus transportation from City Y

Price plus transportation from City X

Market area boundary

Price at X--no transportation

Price at Y--no transportation

City X   -------distance-------   City Y

B

Low-cost transportation

Cost of transfer from one transportation means to another.

NOTE: slope is transportation cost per unit of distance.

City X   -------distance-------   City Y

C

A   B

M₁   M₂

A'   B'

Figure 9B shows how this simple technique might be used in a more complex situation, where the price in y was higher and where some portion of transportation from x was at a lower rate, represented by a flatter slope, but there was also an additional cost in transferring the item from the cheaper to the more expensive form of transportation, represented by a small vertical line.

This method can be expanded from a line to a surface. Figure 9C shows how a series of concentric lines giving cost for procurement from x and y can be drawn. The boundary denoting the area for which x and y are the cheaper sources will pass through the intersections of concentric circles representing identical costs from x and y. Where price and transportation charges in x and y are identical, this boundary will be a straight line; otherwise it will be elliptical, as is shown in Figure 9C.

Determination of Supply Areas
As Part of a Systems Approach

The microanalytic technique for spatial allocation can be expanded to more than two cities, and can be used as one element in a broader analysis. During World War II, Donald O. Hammerberg and his associates at the University of Connecticut approached the collection, processing, and distribution of fluid milk for home consumption in Connecticut as a system problem.[2] The exigencies of war led them to investigate whether a reorganization of the milk industry could more economically meet consumer wants, preserve the well-being of farmers, and economize on the use of labor, transportation, equipment, and fuel.

This study was an example of defining a system according to the particular problem needs. Exogenous to their system concept was the pattern of production by 7,500 dairy farmers, and the needs of 1.7 million consumers. The authors proceeded to identify a system concept of milk collection and distribution, estimating system parameters by engineering-type synthesis and regression analysis to produce functions relating inputs and outputs of the various subsystems. These were then the foundation on which their analysis was based.

Cost of transportation as function of distance was developed for several types of transportation. Farm prices were represented on a map by a series of circles around the various markets, declining with distance from them. Given a price paid at a central point, the price received by a farmer, after transportation costs, declined with distance. The boundary of the milk supply area for any market was at the point where net price just induced farmers to ship to that market rather than some other. This is known as the milkshed.

With so many markets, these constructions become quite complex. Figure 10 shows the least-transportation-cost supply areas for each of fourteen markets, given the pricing, production, and consumption patterns. Farmers on the boundaries receive equal net prices regardless of which market they select. Prices vary, according to the area of the state, the points more distant from major markets receiving the lower prices. The boundaries of milksheds interact with each other in complex manner. If Bridgeport were to seek milk from what had been part of the New Haven supply area, it would lead New Haven to compete more with Meriden, which in turn would compete with adjacent areas. Prices at various markets would move to redirect the existing supply of milk among the various markets.

The least-transportation-cost milksheds were delineated, which were then compared with the cost of existing milksheds to determine what savings might result from a reorganization of milksheds. It was found that revision of milkshed boundaries would reduce the average distance to market from 21.7 to 20.5 miles. However, by reducing the overlap in supply areas for several markets, for example where milk from one district supplied both New Haven and Hartford, the average density of milk collection per mile of truck travel was increased with attendant reduction in costs of collection, and miles travelled by the pick-up trucks. The average saving was .5 cents per cwt. on the distance factor, and 1.6 cents per cwt. on the density factor. Additional savings would have been obtained by reorganization of truck routes.

FIGURE 10

Optimized Milksheds and Price Structure for Connecticut

A.   Revised Milksheds for 14 Connecticut markets

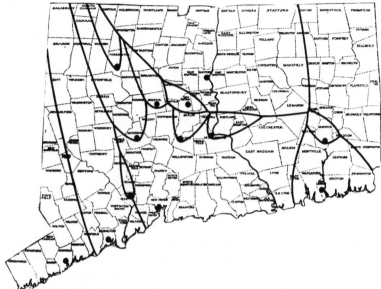

B.   Competitive milk price structure for Connecticut

Source: Storrs Agricultural Experiment Station Bulletin 237

113

The entire analysis is too complex to present
here. It had to take account of the institutional
peculiarities of the milk industry which included
state-administered prices and controlled supply areas.
For example, price regulation had encouraged nonprice
competition and such duplication in service as excessive numbers of retail trucks travelling down the same
suburban streets, each delivering a few quarts. The
distribution of milk from a city plant to stores and
homes is the reverse image of the collection process.
The delivery process, which included assembly of loads,
driving on routes, walking from the truck to the customers' doorsteps, time spent on making collections,
was studied by industrial engineering methods for
type and routes.

Other Spatial Models

The larger a city, the larger is the surrounding
area bound to it by economic ties. The milkshed
boundaries around large cities are explainable by
easily treated marketing decisions by price-oriented
farmers. But milksheds are merely one of a vast complex of interactions between city and noncity, and
among cities. No existing model encompasses all of
these interactions. Many analyses, wherein spatial
distribution is an element, make use of simplified
aggregative relationships. Among these, the so-called
gravity models are frequently used as descriptors of
data. In a simple form, a gravity model might hypo-
thesize that persons at a point intermediate between
two cities would divide their purchases from the two
according to the inverted ratio of the distances
squared, but in direct ratio to the square of the
population of the cities. For systems analysis
purposes, such a model is deficient in that variables
such as population are exogenous to system optimization.
In the milkshed model, both central city price and transportation costs were under some control, and might be
established as a result of a system analysis.

Spatial Optimization and Discontinuous Functions

In the milkshed model used by the Connecticut
researchers, a continuous collection density function

for the quantity of milk per mile of road, was used.
In fact, milk is picked up at particular points where
the farmers leave it, or at the farmsteads. Pick-up
trucks need only travel between a number of specific
points. The driver is interested, therefore, in the
order of pick-up and the route which will minimize
the distance travelled. Analytically, this is comparable to the problem of a travelling salesman who
wishes to complete his route in the least distance.
Either case is an example where the "benefit" is held
constant, because the number of calls is not changed.
The optimum is the "least distance" route. This problem could be solved by "brute force" where there were
only a few calls. If there were four stops plus the
office, every possible permutation of travel paths
could be listed and costed, viz:

Office to customers 1, 2, 3, 4 in that order;

Office to customers 1, 2, 4, 3 in that order;

and so on. Many of the possible path combinations
are obvious nonsense, but if the number of stops were
very large (there are 181,144 alternative routings
among 10 locations), it is highly desirable to use the
techniques of linear programming for an efficient
search for the optimum route. These techniques had
not been developed in 1942, so the Connecticut researchers were obliged to rely on a route density model, and
not explore potential benefits fully from route reorganization.

In a system analysis, optima of this sort might be
used to create a functional relationship of miles travelled as a function of number of stops. The number of
miles in the optimum route for 8, 9, 10, 11, etc., stops
would each be calculated. Depending on the location of
the 10th stop, the order of calls might be very different for 10 than for 9, but each order would be the optimum for that number. It would be translated into a cost
function by applying each mileage to a function of cost
as a function of miles, to give cost of visiting 9, 10,
11 etc. stops.

Techniques for other spatial problems are available. One early example was a study of the routing

of school buses. The number and location of warehouses or district headquarters can be determined by
related methods. Similar methods have been proposed
for allocation of Congressional districts by computer.

SUBOPTIMIZATION

In the milk pick-up example, as in several given
previously, optimization proceeded as a two-stage process. First, an optimum route was established subject
to the constraint of a given number of stops. Then
the number of stops was varied, to see how cost related
to number. The result was easily translated into a cost
function. Benefit is presumably some function of number
of stops. The first optimum was, therefore, a simple
form of suboptimization.

The term suboptimization has unfairly acquired a
bad connotation. Indeed, suboptimization is essential
to bring large complex systems problems to manageable
proportions. Suboptimization need not lead to faulty
results if analysis proceeds step by step to the larger problem, but there are dangers. In the words of
Robert E. Machol, "The principle of suboptimization
states that optimization of each subsystem independently will not in general lead to a system optimum
and, more strongly that improvement of a particular
system may actually worsen the overall system."[3]
Suboptimization at its best is the conscious result
of analysis in terms of a model that encompasses only
part of a larger problem, with the intent of examining interrelations between submodels at a later stage.

CONCLUSIONS ON OPTIMIZATION

In nonprobablistic cost-effectiveness formula-
tions, the configuration yielding the maximum net
benefit (that is, gross benefit minus cost--on the
assumption that the system will be operated as efficiently as possible) is typically the optimum system
configuration. Frequently, the techniques of microeconomics will produce highly useful results, making
use of relatively easy and widely understood techniques.

For practical purposes, the configuration which apparently cannot be significantly improved upon may be accepted as the optimum. Frequently, only a small number of system configurations can be fully explored. Taking the "best" of these as the optimum may involve some risk of overlooking a better choice, which can be reduced if the analysts have tried a priori to include their hunch as to the real optimum among the configurations analyzed, and they are sufficiently astute to make good hunches. The term "satisficing" has been used to describe the terminating of efforts when further refinements do not seem worth the analytical effort.

There are many optimization problems which, however, involve specific constraints, or limits that cannot be exceeded. Here the methods of linear programming will be highly useful. The conceptual statement of a linear programming problem is straightforward, and modern computer programs make the solution, even of large problems, far from alarming.

Not uncommonly, the use of continuous functions deviates from reality, for example where only discrete quantities of inputs are available, or where inputs can be used only in certain ratios. Sometimes it is useful to assume continuous functions nonetheless, although methods are available for linear programming which will constrain the solution to integral values.

Uncertainty is frequently a characteristic of optimization problems. Methods of making optimal decisions in the face of uncertainty have been noted, including, as part of the game theory, the uncertain response of some opponent to the choice of a system or strategy.

Note might be made of the static-dynamic model choice and its implications for optimization. The examples given are of the easier static forms of analysis. These may fail to identify how a system must change over time to remain an optimum system in the face of changing conditions. In addition to continuing adjustment to trends, a system should not itself lead to or contribute to cyclical behavior. In the

methodology of industrial dynamics there are means
for exploring this possibility.

Despite the wide variety of optimization techniques, the limits to our ability to identify optima
are very real. First, even formal analytical models
can be very difficult. Second, as models are invariably simplifications, an optimum identified by a model
may not be appropriate. It may be a suboptimization
because of inappropriately limited scope or an inappropriate statement of objections. In any event, optima
flow from the data on which they are based, and where
data may be questioned, so can be the results, provided that the characteristics of the optima as identified
are sensitive to probable errors in the data.

It is always of concern lest a so-called optimum
merely results from arbitrary assumptions concealed
by analytical camouflage. The structure of a system
analysis will, for this reason, always be of concern
to the decision-maker. Sometimes the effects of necessarily arbitrary assumptions may be explored by
sensitivity analysis. Net benefits often do not
change markedly with small changes in discount rates
or system characteristics, and sometimes they are
not sensitive even to drastic changes. In short, the
analytical effort of seeking a precise optimum is
affected by diminishing returns.

NOTES TO CHAPTER 6

[1]von Neumann and Morgenstern, op. cit.

[2]D.O. Hammerberg, L.W. Parker, and R.G. Bressler,
Jr., Efficiency of Milk Marketing in Connecticut:
Supply and Price Interrelationships for Fluid Milk
Markets, Bulletin 237 (Storrs, Connecticut: Univer-
sity of Connecticut, February 1942).

[3]Robert E. Machol, ed., Systems Engineering
Handbook (New York: McGraw-Hill, 1965).

CHAPTER **7** DATA NEEDS AND

SYSTEMS ANALYSIS

    Factual information is needed in systems analy-
sis for several purposes. First, the subject must be
sufficiently understood so that a working hypothesis
of a system model can be formulated. Here, breadth
and perspective are initially important--a spectrum
of facts and insight into causal relationships from
which a model can be constructed.

    The contributions of persons who have been involved
in the subject matter, either as operators, recipients
of its benefits, as suppliers of inputs, or as professional students, are particularly important sources at
this time. Systems analysts, who may be skilled in
analytical technique but ignorant of subject matter,
must interact with such persons and evolve a system
model with their assistance. This is a crucial and
difficult phase of systems analysis. By constructing
a model, an analyst states an elaborate theory of
relationships, and of ways in which system forces can
be manipulated to produce desired results. His efforts
are bound to appear incomplete, as the selectivity
inherent in any system concept will exclude relationships that, from some points of view, are important.
It is unlikely that systems analysts will be able to
match the sophistication of the subject matter experts.
Analysts are almost certain to appear presumptuous,
and to be resented.

    The system model may, indeed, go through several
iterations as the initial model is evaluated and tested.
Much of this testing depends on the numerical estimation of the parameters of the model, and of trial runs

of the model as simulation exercises at rates of operation expected in real life. Thus, the second need for
data, the quantification of parameters, is related to the
first, and the third need, the establishment of real-life
values of inputs, outputs, and rate of operation is also
related.

QUANTIFICATION OF MODELS

Parameter Estimation

How models are to be used for optimization has significance for data needs. Suppose that an optimum is to
be identified from a model by marginal analysis. For
this analytical technique, it is data on the incremental
changes in costs and benefits that serve a useful analytical purpose. Nothing would be gained, for example,
from estimates of costs common to all system configurations which were cancelled out in intersystem comparisons.
If the analytical technique will be linear programming,
data on capacity constraints will be needed; decision-
theoretic models will require estimates of probabilities.

Basically, parameters can be quantified in three
ways. Of these, statistical analysis of observed, but
uncontrolled, real life will generally be the principal
recourse for systems that involve people and existing
institutions. The techniques of statistical estimation
by multiple regression analysis are indispendable wher-
ever control over the observed subject matter is limited,
and there are many variables.

The second method is controlled experimentation in
the classic pattern of the physical sciences. Indeed,
some behavioral science results have been obtained
in this way.

The third source of parameters is the body of
known relationships either from basic theoretical
principles, or past empirical observation.

Parameters from Regression Analysis

In recent years, particularly among econometricians, awareness has grown that the parameter estimates

that gave the best linear unbiased estimates of the
value of a dependent variable from several independent
variables were not necessarily the best estimates of
the structural parameters of a model. As a model is a
structure, it is the latter that are wanted in systems
analysis. That a nonstructural, reduced-form estimating equation may have considerable value for predicting
is not always relevant.

The use of data to establish real-life values of
the structural parameters of a system model may run
into problems of a most fundamental sort, depending
on the form of the model. There are, indeed, theoretical reasons why structural parameters may not be
obtainable from the data. Difficulties in this respect
were first widely discussed in relation to demand functions. According to the famous "law of supply and
demand," market price and volume of business are established at a point where a demand function and a supply
function intersect. If either the demand or supply
function shifts, there can be a different observation.
If a least-squares regression is fitted to a series
of related prices and quantities, as observed at different times, the result is ambiguous in that if there
had been shifts in both functions, the result can not
be interpreted either as a demand or supply function.
The parameters of the regression are not structural,
and the form of the regression does not correspond to
a theoretically valid model of demand and supply.

In the above example, identification of structural
parameters of the demand and supply functions would
have been possible if the model had contained additional
exogenous variables. The analyst may be restricted in
his attempt to reach the goal of parameter identification by the unavailability of data for such additional
variables; he gains nothing by including in his model
variables which could theoretically lead to structural
identification, but for which there are no data. If
the quality of data on these additional variables is
uncertain, the resulting uncertainty and error will
be reflected in the numerical estimates for all parameters in the model, as they are all derived as part of
an interrelated group.

Quite frequently data must be sampled. This in itself is a source of random and biasing errors. The random error problem is as simple as this: If black balls and white balls are picked from an urn containing precisely equal numbers of each and nothing predisposes the picker to select one color over the other, there is still a strong possibility that any sample of balls will not contain black and white in equal proportions. The distribution of sample content can be stated precisely, and leads to a statement as to how large a sample must be to reduce the risk that it is not representative.

In the same way, data on which a regression is based may not be representative, merely as a result of the sampling distribution even in the absence of any biasing tendency. If it is not, estimates of the parameters derived from that data will be somewhat in error. The likely range of that error can be estimated. The only way to reduce it is to enlarge the size of the sample. While the likelihood of nonrepresentativeness of the population from which the sample was drawn can be reduced thereby, it is never eliminated.

Regressions From Aggregative Data

Not infrequently, the available data are aggregates or averages from many sources, differing in size and in the manner in which they are influenced by the variables in the system model. Yet many of the theories on which models might be based, including most marginal analysis, are directly applicable only to individual decision-making units. The assumption that marginal analysis can be directly applied to industry data, and that parameters so derived are relevant to optimization, is not always conceptually sound. For example, how a businessman would respond to a price increase may well be explained by his demand function relative to his cost function. However, when demand and cost functions are averages of an entire industry in which some members have high costs, others low costs, some use modern equipment and others equipment on the verge of obsolescence, the marginal technique may not "explain" industry-wide data movements--and model parameters

developed to fit industry data are correspondingly
irrelevant to any one firm. What are needed are either:
(1) models that are fully valid for aggregates--and
theories to support these are particularly difficult--
or (2) data for individual firms or decision-making
units, data which may be unavailable. This is one
reason why systems analysts must so frequently gather
fresh data, despite volumes of published aggregative
data.

Parameters from Engineering and Science

It is known from physics how the loss of electric
power through a transmission system is related to the
length, diameter, and material of the wires conducting
electricity from one point to another. It would be
ridiculous to conduct a statistical analysis of actual
transmission lines in order to develop design parameters
for these attributes of a transmission system. Quite
frequently, some part of a system model is based on
physical relationships, for which such information
sources are appropriate. While rarely possible in
the real world, behavioral scientists do sometimes
simulate psychological or sociological relationships
under controlled laboratory conditions and may thereby
come up with comparable information. Some of the basic
relationships in a teaching machine system theory have
been developed from controlled experiments.

The classic purpose of scientific experimentation,
the generation of data through experimentation, is
sometimes used in support of systems analysis. It has,
of course, always been common for engineers to establish empirical relationships in support of engineering
design by experimentation. Even in nonsystems-oriented
Federal programs, "demonstration projects" and "pilot
projects" are undertaken partly for the purpose of
quantifying relationships. From the systems point of
view, a demonstration project may be justified by the
data generated relative to the costs involved. Experiments are expensive, and it is up to the analyst to
show that they contribute to system design commensu-
rately with their cost. Too often, however, social
experiments are conducted under uncontrolled conditions,

with insufficient attention to the "instrumentation."
Demonstration project-type experiments thereby fail
to produce definitive information.

THE EXTENT OF DATA NEEDS

Quantity of Data

Where a critical statistic is unavailable, the
complete systems analysis is likely to have certain
flaws which may not be obvious in summary reports.
Where many data are unavailable, it will be difficult
to carry a systems analysis beyond the conceptual
stage. But on the other hand, a system model can be
tailored to availability of data. Where lack of data,
time, and funds limit the types of data that can be
developed, it may still be useful to conceive of a
system as a simple structure, with relatively few
variables.

By limiting volume of data to what is needed,
perhaps more complete models can be developed. It
may be useful to examine trade-offs between models
with a few parameters specified accurately versus
rougher estimates of more. How many data are enough
depends on the degree of accuracy sought for the
various parameters of the model. Insights into needs
for statistical accuracy can be sought by sensitivity
analyses, designed to explore how the results of analysis are affected by errors in particular parameters
or rate of operation specification: It is quite likely
that some parameters will be more important than others,
and that, therefore, the degree of accuracy to be sought
for various parameters will differ. While sampling
theory gives considerable guidance to the size of
samples necessary to establish parameters with a given
degree of accuracy, the means for exploiting the power
of the theory are not always available.

Data Bias

More serious than inaccuracy is that data may
reflect a bias. Bias, by definition, produces results

that are incorrect in some systematic way. Bias may
result from the difficulties in training reliable
reporters or from faulty analytical techniques. Not
infrequently, too little is known of the population
from which a sample is drawn to ensure lack of bias,
nor can sampling procedures always be developed that
do not themselves inject a bias. The impact on the
data source from the use made of data may be a source
of bias. This issue may first come to the fore at
the time when a statistical series, previously merely
a descriptive statistic, becomes an operating statistic.
There have been examples of sudden discontinuities in
data series coinciding with a new operations use. It
is reported that the amount of earthquake damage reported on public buildings increased greatly when Federal
loans or outright grants became available at favorable
terms for the repair of damage. The analyst will generally feel more comfortable where data is obtained
from persons not associated with operating programs,
but this is rarely possible. It is often more practical to tighten up reporting criteria and to rely
on review and auditing.

Better reports do not necessarily mean more
reports. The quantity of data can often be reduced
in favor of fewer of higher quality. Indeed, a systems analysis may point in this direction by indicating which data can be omitted, as having no particular
relevance to operating decisions. Since administration
is based on reports, there is a general need for meaningful, accurate, unbiased data on operations for
operating as well as for system analytical purposes.

Where data are generated by nonstatistical
methods, e.g., engineering design estimates, there
is generally little basis for evaluating the accuracy
or bias in the results, other than to repeat designs
independently, to see whether additional design groups
reach the same results as the first.

VALIDATION OF A SYSTEM CONCEPT

A system concept, reduced to the form of a model,
expressed with some degree of formality, and with

parameters quantified through whatever skill the
analyst can muster, is an analytical and predictive
engine. On the one hand, it may express the resources
needed by an efficient, optimized system to create a
given quantity of benefits. On the other hand, it may
predict the benefits that are obtainable, given certain
resource availabilities.

The model, of course, merely indicates what could
be done if the system of the model were created. As
it is a hypothetical construction both as to form and
as to particular values of parameters, it is quite
necessary that it be scrutinized with care. One of
the more useful ways to do this is to simulate the
operation of the system described in the model, as
it would operate in real life. The validity of a
system model may be finally tested when the system
is put in operation. Such a test is of academic
interest. The practical man will seek to validate
a system concept before committing substantial
resources to it.

Simulation depends upon models with parameters
of functional relationships and forms of functional
relationships which reflect the real world. If
either the form of the model or parameters are in
error, simulations will not be meaningful. It should
be clear whether the simulation is of what <u>could</u> be
obtained, or what <u>will be</u> obtained by operation of
the system.

Models may be constructed as if they were purely
deterministic, where in fact there are random elements
in the relationship on the understanding that the
models refer to average values. For these, one simulation is sufficient to give the result for certain
values representing real life. Models may also be
constructed that explicitly include randomness in
relationships. Here, successive trials of the same
experiment will not always yield the same result,
and simulations must be repeated often enough to
create a distribution of outputs.

Since the future is unpredictable, simulation
must be run for many possible futures. Suppose the
frequency distribution of the values which some

variable might take is known. In successive trials,
values of the variable are assigned according to
this distribution. These values may then be fed
into a simulator in order to obtain the frequency
distribution of outputs. The simulation of random
events or a relationship with a stochastic element
is often conducted by what is known as the "Monte
Carlo Method." Monte Carlo is very frequently a
computer technique from which very large numbers of
trials are generated.

The validation of a model by simulation is not
equivalent, however, to testing the optimality of
system design. Analysis of proposed small changes
in a system in being, to see whether changes produce
some improvement, is one test for optimization. If
they do, optimization was not achieved.

An ability to predict system performance in
advance, to forestall the possibility of casting
errors into concrete, is of great value. The techniques
for doing so are integral with system design. Properly
constructed and carried out, modeling simulation may
greatly improve the ability of decision-makers to
visualize the performance of a system, especially in
unusual situations. Computerized simulations can
be repeated, at modest cost, for a tremendous variety
of situations. Real-life gaming is more expensive
and, therefore, likely to be limited, but is also
more likely to uncover unanticipated relationships
of importance. Players not committed to the system
concept in advance are more likely to uncover
pitfalls in system design than a programmed computerized
simulation.

CONCLUSION

In undertaking a systems analysis, it is well to
stress the vital importance of information and data
for the creation of a system concept, for translating
it from generality to specificness, and for obtaining
insights as to how it will work in practice--in short,
its basic validity.

A potential source of difficulty in systems analysis is the basically different orientation and training of the model builder and the person who is expert at data generation. Indeed, the generalist, who is indispensable in the evolution of a system concept, may not be in successful communications with the statistician, who can alone estimate system parameters (provided he has an appropriate model) from real life, or with the engineer or hard scientist who may produce parameter estimates from design technique and theory. Many model builders are oriented toward abstract principles and lack the patience to deal with data and the problems of data collection. It is in econometrics that an integrated sophistication in model building, data gathering, and analysis has gone furthest. Not much of this has yet penetrated to the hardware-oriented systems analyst. On the other hand, econometricians and economists, with a few exceptions, have not understood engineering methods of parameter generation.

The validity of models depends on a general understanding of a system in its environment. A generalized but nonquantified system concept may, in fact, be highly useful and supportive of administrative decisions. To move beyond this step, to a system model with quantified parameters is often very difficult and delayed by the necessity of developing the most fundamental data. Perhaps more attention has been given to quantifying the parameters of macroeconomic models than any other single model, yet even here the numbers are often subject to questioning--as are the forms of the models themselves.

Of course, existing sources should be used to the fullest, but systems analysts must sometimes face the need for expensive procedures for data generation. While marginal costs and benefit data are rarely available a priori, the chances of finding useful data are better for costs than for benefits. Cost analysis is intimately related to financial control. Unfortunately, much of the effort that goes into arbitrary allocations of fixed costs, i.e., for rate regulation, not only has no significance for systems analysis, but even substantially reduces the usefulness

of published data. It may be possible, if the basic
data from which arbitrary allocations are made can
be obtained, to "cleanse" available cost data of
arbitrary allocations, and thereby make them suitable
for systems analytical purposes.

As a practical matter models must often be cut
to the cloth that available data provides.

CHAPTER **8** AFTER SYSTEMS ANALYSIS

Assume that the results of a systems analysis are in hand. Objectives have been identified, the scope and the physical form of a system have been established with the help of a series of cost-benefit comparisons. The time stream of net benefits was found to yield a satisfactory return, and the financial requirements for procuring the system hardware were within bounds. The systems analysts had succeeded in developing a concept acceptable to major elements of the body politic despite differing views as to policy objectives, and some personage or group has accepted the task of shepherding the system to ultimate implementation.

As a result of the analysis, some configuration was selected as better promoting objectives than alternative configurations. To some degree, this was identified by formal optimization, but an administrative judgment took into account the validity of the concept of objectives used by system analysts, interactions between the system and the outside environment, and the administrators' views of practical reality, political feasibility, the availability of financial support, the priority of the system resource requirements vis-à-vis competing demands.

In order to implement a system, two types of planning are necessary. On the one hand, at this point the system configuration is likely to be rather general. Before implementation can proceed, systems specifications must be translated into subsystem specifications, and details resolved that while they would not have a major impact on system adoption,

must yet be settled. A typical system concept does
not draw entirely from off-the-shelf subsystems.
New engineering, perhaps even some advance in technology, may be necessary. The environment surrounding
the system may have to be more thoroughly investigated.

On the other hand, a detailed plan for implementation must be worked out. The schedule is a focal
point of this plan. The principal phases are research
and development, production of the physical hardware
of the system, negotiation with parties whose con-
currence is needed, development of an implementing
organization, and actual operation of the completed
system. Each of these steps must be scheduled in
detail, as must the order in which they can be
accomplished. Administrative arrangements for
coordination, authorization, review, and control
must be promulgated. With governmental systems,
there must be legislative authority and budget
authorization.

Naturally enough, persons who use formal
analytical techniques to create a system concept will
be inclined to apply them also to the manner in which
that concept is transformed into reality. Aside from
a natural enthusiasm for broadening the scope of
analysis, system implementation is a complex, difficult
task. The managing group will be fully aware from
the complexity of the concept and perhaps from other
past experiences, of the importance of a sound
organization of their task, and the issues to be
settled in the creation of a managerial organization
for systems implementation. Among the points to
be considered are:

- the scope of management authority

- its system responsibilities

- responsibilities it will have other than
  this system

- authority to resolve difference between
  contributing parties to system implementation

- by whom will performance be monitored
  and rewarded

- role of existing organizations

- if a new organization is created, how
  it will be staffed

- provision for every phase of system
  implementation

The feasibility of assigning system management
responsibility to an existing organization is not to
be overlooked. The use of an existing structure
will avoid delays in assembling a cadre, in developing
an integrated team, and in whatever legal and administrative approvals would be necessary in creating
a new organization. Even where an existing organization
does not match the system management task, it may be
possible to transform it into a system management
team by assigning it systems responsibility while at
the same time withdrawing other responsibilities so
that it can concentrate on the system. Yet there may
be problems. Unless this system really replaces
responsibilities any existing organization will
already have, its interest in the system will be
diluted. If successful management of the system is
of overwhelming importance, it may be desirable that
it be managed by persons with no conflicting or
distracting responsibilities. Surely some compromises
are necessary for every program, but they are likely
to dilute the system when the system management group
is a less-than-whole-hearted proponent of its responsibility.

Then also, a system development task must probably
be advanced by the joint effort of a number of organizations, conceivably bureaus in several departments
of the Federal Government. If each of these has a
number of responsibilities, the management problem is
magnified. The question as to which should assume the
central coordinating role may be vexing. Coordination
that is merely persuasive or permissive will have
limited impact on the priority assigned to the system
by the various contributors. Systems can, in fact,

be developed and implemented as a coordinated effort
of functionally independent agencies. Not infrequently,
however, the price of seeking coordination and agency
autonomy simultaneously is delay and inefficiency.
If one agency decides unilaterally, for internal
reasons, to reduce its effort in support of the system,
and the efforts of others cannot proceed until it has
completed its task, that decision produces ramifica-
tions in other agencies. Another possibility is that
one agency, for internal reasons, decides that it
dislikes the agreed-upon system characteristics and
arbitrarily alters them, or declines to proceed with
its portion of the work until its point of view is
agreed upon.

Thus, if systems approaches are to be applied
in government, there will be persuasive administrative
reasons for either restricting system concepts to the
jurisdictional bounds of a particular agency under
some degree of centralized control, or strengthening
the hand of interdepartmental management. In this
way, the objective structure to which the systems
management is directed can be greatly simplified.
The problems of interagency coordination arise to
a considerable degree as the result of differences
in the objective structures of different governmental
agencies. These differences are often written into
law.

The standard prescription for overcoming such
difficulties is, of course, to increase the authority
and power of a central manager, who is able to enforce
his point of view and control the allocation of manpower and other resources. Certain powers are more
critical than others. Probably the most important is
financial control, including authority to advance or
withhold funds according to whether work is appropriate and on schedule. Almost as important is the power
to select among performers--to reassign work from a
balky agency to another, or to an outside private
contractor

It is also helpful, if not vital, that a system
manager have line-management-authority over the personnel concerned with the system; in short, the

authority to approve promotions, to hire and fire.
In this way the performance criteria applied to individuals are relevant to the system itself.

The essence of the system management approach
and the purpose of system management is the implementation of the system, as an overriding goal. From
one standpoint, it represents a specialized type of
decentralized management. The system manager in an
organization which is larger than the system itself
has a system task that is one phase of an organization's
larger program.

As applied to government operations, many systems
concepts might be so defined as to coincide with the
jurisdictions of existing agencies. Transportation
responsibilities have been highly fractionated within
the Federal Government, for example. That it was
meaningful and potentially advantageous to treat transportation as a national system argued strongly for a
centralized administrative structure. Creating a
Department of Transportation has simplified system
of a national transportation complex, but the Interstate Commerce Commission and the Maritime Commission
were left outside the structure. The problem of interagency coordination, before national transportation
can be implemented or planned as a system, remains.
Also left out are transportation regulatory and planning functions of state and local governments.

The implementation of system approaches which
overlap the responsibility of the Federal and state
Governments seem inevitably to create unresolvable
political dilemmas. While within the Federal structure a chief executive exercises nominal authority
over every other line executive, his authority does
not extend to the chief executives of state governments. Yet a large and perhaps increasing number of
major social problems seem to call for a systems
approach which cuts across Federal-local administrative
boundaries. This is surely the case in welfare programs, manpower training and education programs, model
city programs, and transportation programs. A case in
point would be the management and control of the water
resources associated with the Great Lakes. Several

states, by their use or pollution of lake water,
affect the welfare of each other. Thus, the control
of lake pollution is an interstate and Federal
problem. A Great Lakes Commission could be established,
could conceive of the management of the lake resources
as a system, and would seek to implement programs,
permissively, but only those which were to the benefit
of each state relative to its cost burden. Such a
restraint may to some degree rule out feasible
approaches that might produce a greater national
net benefit, although also producing a transfer of
benefit from one state to another.

These comments place in focus the frequent
complaint of state and local governments that it is
difficult to deal with the multiplicity of potential
program funding sources within the Federal structure.
The state or local jurisdiction that has conceived
of a system-like solution to some problem in a manner
that cuts across jurisdictional lines within the
Federal establishment encounters particular difficulties.
It quickly becomes aware that it is proposing a program
for which no agency feels a comprehensive interest
nor necessarily finds it within its legal bounds
to support. It may be obliged to restrict its approach
to the bounds of some agency's interest.

It may be possible under these circumstances to
organize joint support by a number of different
departments. But who is to take the leadership in
arranging that funding? Clearly, the state government
has the principal interest; yet it seems anomalous,
to say the least, that a state government, the solicitor
of Federal funds, should take the leadership in
producing a coordination between Federal departments.
In fact, Federal departments frequently do take interagency coordinating leadership, and transfers of
funds from one department to another in support of
programs which are of interest to both are common.
The potential problems with this approach are manageable
with small, simple programs. In practice, the departments which have provided some funds but exercise no
administrative control directly often become dissatisfied
with the arrangement. Yet satisfactory efforts have
been implemented in this way.

There are, in fact, few well-defined mechanisms
for interdepartmental and intergovernmental implementation of system concepts that cut across established
jurisdictional bounds in the existing structure of
the Federal Government that would produce the degree
of centralized authority required under a systems
management approach. One approach to interagency
coordination would be to assign leadership to the
Executive Office. The principal agency of the
Executive Office, the Bureau of the Budget, is
traditionally circumspect as to the authority which
it exercises over other departments. The Executive
Office is really a staff agency that can influence
the Chief Executive rather than a line authority,
and its position endows it with the classical weakness
of staff as opposed to line. Further, as Richard E.
Neustadt has pointed out, the independence of the
heads of departments and major agencies is enhanced
by their direct access to the President and the
autonomous political base that department heads
often have.[1]

The essence of the systems management approach
is, of course, the coordination of interfunctional
efforts as a line responsibility. Efforts to strengthen
the direct managerial authority of the Executive
Office of the President are viewed with much trepidation,
as an infringement on a balance of powers, maintained
not merely between the three principal branches of
government but between the various departments and
agencies of the Executive Branch.

SCHEDULES FOR IMPLEMENTATION

The scheduling problem is a good example of the
manner in which systems analysis interfaces with
system management and of how systems analysis extends
beyond the problem of optimum system design. What
is optimum may depend on the implementation plan.
Suppose that aside from differences in implementation
there were two close contenders--one of which would
produce some benefits when the system was still only
partially implemented while the other ultimately
produced a greater net benefit but only after the

system was fully complete. The greater time-discounting
of the longer-postponed benefits might work to the
advantage of the system that gave some benefit immediately.

    The Program Evaluation and Review Technique (PERT)
reflects its development as a tool for implementation
of a single, nonrepeated task. PERT is a means of
representing in network form an implementation plan
that has been developed for a multistage task. The
total of a "system" task is broken down into subtasks,
represented graphically as paths between nodes in a
network, the nodes being well-defined events in the
program with arrowheads indicating direction of effect.
Thus arrowheads leading into any event identify,
on the one hand, all the immediately prior activities
that must be completed before it is achieved, and on
the other hand arrows pointing out identify all the
activities which can proceed only after the event has
taken place. Estimates are made of time for the
transition between nodes, perhaps by taking a weighted
average of the longest possible time, the shortest
possible time, and the most likely, the latter being
given more weight than the extremes. In early PERT
analysis, stereotyped assumptions were usually made
of the frequency distribution of possible times to
complete a path; it has been recognized that an
underestimate may result from this practice.

    From a network with estimated times for individual
activities, it is possible to estimate time for the
entire program, target dates for completion of each
task, and for final completion. The duration of the
whole system implementation program is, of course,
the sum of times along the most time-consuming path
through the network. Any delay in tasks along this
critical path will delay the entire project. Other
paths contain "slack"--where delays will not delay
the project unless they exceed the amount of slack.
Since slack is, up to a point, a free good, it is
attractive to consider shifting resources from
activities with slack time to those along the critical
path, seeking thereby to minimize critical path time.
But slack time is not entirely free, because there
is, in fact, some probability of schedule slippage
exceeding slack on noncritical paths.

PERT networks are simple, or intricate, depending on how many events and activities a program is broken down into. While nearly any activity can be broken down into finer subactivities, each terminating in an event, one should, at least informally, cost-benefit any elaboration of detail beyond relatively simple networks. It has been suggested that a network should be developed with events occurring about as frequently as major management reviews. While begging the question of how frequently management reviews are necessary, and how this may be affected by PERT this points out a significant interaction between PERT and management.

Use of PERT imposes additional scheduling and planning tasks on systems management. For example, completion of an event must be precisely defined if progress reports are to be fudge-proof. How the events of a system relate to each other must be carefully described.

The program schedule finally hit upon in actual analysis is the result of a series of trial PERTs, interspersed with analysis and trial shifts of resources. This may be done by a computer program or by hand. Pessimistic as well as expected times can be used for such exercises, in order to obtain an estimate of possible slippage, or of how activities might be scheduled so as to minimize the risk of slippage. As actual path times become history during the course of a project, PERT is redone to obtain revised estimates of completion date, or new insights as to threats to the schedule. Schedules may be rearranged, and resources be allocated as a result of such analysis. In this way continuing analysis supports and lends flexibility to the system management task.

The argument has been advanced that the additional effort of organizing, planning, scheduling work for PERT network preparation has merit in its own right, regardless of any use made of the results. Task definition as required by PERT clarifies for parties on each side of an intersubsystem interface what they need from each other. Indeed, it is not clear whether such effects or the actual use of PERT as

a review and control device is responsible for the
improvements in schedule-keeping that seem sometimes
to result from PERT.

There is, of course, a large family of other
scheduling and project control techniques. The
Gantt chart, a widely known example, is a vertical
list of subtasks followed by columns corresponding
to schedule intervals. The dates of initiation and
completion of each task are shown with markers to
indicate principal events along the way. Another
scheduling method, Line of Balance, gives a cross-
sectional view of a continuing activity in which
work progresses through a series of stages, so that
a delay in one stage may affect the entire operation.

SYSTEM IMPLEMENTATION AND MANAGERIAL CONTROL

Cost and benefit estimates are, in the first
instance, the basis for system choice. But system
cost estimates are the most important information
for the financial management of a system. Managing
the time profile of expenditures is a particular
responsibility of financial management, which must
rely on engineering and production management
for estimates of the rate at which resources will
be used in the creation of system hardware, on
matériel management for estimates of the cost of
materials incorporated into the system, and so on.

In the Federal structure there are unique
critical points in the financial plan: stages in
planning by the initiating department or agency;
the Bureau of the Budget reviews, inclusion in the
annual fiscal year appropriation request (or supple-
mental appropriation); the authorization by Congress
to undertake a specified effort; the appropriation
of funds for that effort; the award of a contract
in a certain amount; authorization for the contractor
to proceed up to a certain point; submission of bills
or vouchers by the contractor; their review, and
authorization to the Treasury for disbursement. The
process differs somewhat for in-house work and may
differ according to the type of contract.

An extension of PERT technique, known as PERT/COST, uses the activity breakdown developed for time estimating as the structure for project cost estimating. This makes sense: At best, it would be duplicative and confusing to generate separate task structures for scheduling and for costs. Further, time overruns are generally associated with cost overruns; PERT/COST highlights this association.

The purpose of a financial plan is, of course, managerial control. On the one hand, this may mean acquisition of sufficient but not excessive cash balances, authorization, and funding, without excessive reserves that may thereby reduce the availability of funds for another purpose. On the other hand, it may mean tailoring system specifications and development schedules to available financial resources, perhaps altering the work schedule to match the flow of available funding or tailoring system specifications to total available resources.

Above all, managerial control over system implementation must be suitable to a process that is not merely dynamic in the sense of being in motion, but is undergoing a continual evolution, moving from one phase of implementation to another. The nature of resources used, the type of work being performed at the moment, are constantly changing. The managerial control task is not that of maintaining smooth operation of a fairly routine process, as would be the case of a manufacturing operation.

Managerial control flows, of course, from the evaluation of information on operations, and part of a control system is obtaining information relevant to managerial decisions or actions. Assume that there is an a priori system development plan, and the periodic reports as to adherence or nonadherence to the plan. As the plan would provide for movement from phase to phase, on a schedule, specifying ever-changing results, using specific resources, the information flow descriptive of these results would change in content from report to report.

In designing a managerial information system,
using the techniques of systems analysis, selection
of information should be based on the relevancy of
various types of feedback information to the goals
of the system being implemented. For example, the
financial management of any organization will usually
have well-developed procedures for monitoring the
level of expenditure and indicating the degree to
which the organization is using resources, either
more or less rapidly than was budgeted. A review
of this information may cause new instructions
as to system implementation. Not infrequently
there is a change in the financial resources for
system implementation after the program gets under
way, which must be translated into instructions for
all who are contributing to the system.

If the financial information channel were the
only feedback loop, the tendency would be to adjust
the performance of the organization to conform to
financial plans and financial goals, to the possible
neglect of other and more significant goals. In a
private business, where financial results are of
primary importance, this emphasis may be quite appropriate. It is, in fact, reflected in the growing
strength of the controller function in management.
But even business recognizes the dangers in orienting
the guidance of an organization too excessively
toward financial control. In business, financial
management has a tendency to be myopic toward new
product development, for example, or any effort for
which results are imperfectly predictable.

In governmental programs, excessive reliance
on the budgetary or controllership function also
carries possible dangers of overemphasis of financial
criteria. An obvious solution is to make certain
that there is in fact a flow of a broad spectrum of
progress reports with sufficient influential feedback loops that report on other than financial results.

It does, indeed, take some imagination to obtain
an all-inclusive list of resources needed for a full
system program (and the more thoroughly this is done
the worse the system looks on a cost-benefit basis!).

Incomplete identification of costs is common in the
procurement of computer systems, for example. The
extensive preparation for the use of a computer--
known as software--is frequently underestimated, with
the result that the proud possessor is not in a
position to employ his new computer effectively or
completely.

STAFFING FOR A SYSTEMS APPROACH

The question of who is to implement a systems
approach may have to be decided pragmatically by
where the manpower is. At first, the manpower
needed will be weighted toward systems analysts.
A priori, an organization needs to balance its
implementation concept against the rate of analytical
output that its staff can produce--in particular, by
not expecting too much too soon.

Where will the manpower come from? There are
several main routes: making use of available
personnel with whatever skills they may possess;
upgrading them by training courses; bringing into
the organization new, skilled personnel; or contracting
out for analytical work with firms that have a
systems analytical capability. This latter approach
has been used extensively.

Critical in this is that the organization for
creation of the system--and the tasks undertaken at
various phases of its development--have no long-run
future. There is no career in the development of one
particular system, and career development criteria
for personal performance transcend the interest of
a system development manager. Hence, a systems
approach does not fit well a concept of a stable,
career-oriented bureaucracy. One recurring problem
with creating a managerial organization for the
implementation of a single system is that, when the
task is completed, it ceases to serve any useful
purpose. It will be known as a time-limited job,
often unattractive to persons interested in job
security although perhaps attractive to others who
seek only a temporary assignment--as many business

and academic personnel do in government. There are,
however, systems careers for persons who can migrate
from system to system, from employer to employer.
The aerospace industry has partially solved this
problem through job mobility, adaptation to unstable
employment patterns and has attempted to spread the
risk by contracting with a large number of potential
funders of systems. The solution for government may
be a cadre of career systems analysts and managers
in the image of the military or foreign service.

     Profit and nonprofit contract research organizations
are available which have on their staffs personnel
with a demonstrated systems capability, and who have
supplied such analyses in the past. Most aerospace
contractors have a system analytical capability.
These sources tend to differ in experience and orientation. The contract research organizations are
accustomed to modest, relatively short-term contracts
for analysis of a wide variety of problems, often only
part of a systems analysis. Many of these firms spe-
cialize in certain types of analyses. Some organizations who have had their principal experience in military systems may be short on sophistication in dealing
with problems where sociology is important, or which
involve intergovernment, interagency coordination, or
the byplay of nondefense economic life.

     Increasingly, the aerospace companies have broad-
ened the scope of their applications into nondefense
areas. Most have done this selectively: As manufacturers, these companies are not inclined to consider
systems analyses as end products, but hope that they
will be the preliminary to large R&D or production
contracts. Many aerospace firms have approached
system analytical possibilities in nondefense government in such a light. However, they often have particular competence in developing and implementing
imaginative new hardware concepts, from the first
glimmering to the last retrofit. As the transition
from analysis to implementation often leads to trouble
because of changes in staff and organization, this
unity may be highly advantageous.

     The need for a systems capability within govern-
ment cannot be avoided by contracting for systems

analysis and management, though it can surely be reduced. In order to prepare requests for system proposals from contractors, and to monitor the results of contracts, a government agency must have some systems capability within its own shop. And against the pros of contract work must be set such disadvantages as higher cost, lack of continuity in analytical teams, more difficulty in changing the orientation of a study defined in a contract in midstream, problems of confidentiality, and conflict of interest.

In avoiding these difficulties by use of an in-house group, other problems may be encountered. For example, what is gained in flexibility during the course of a study may be offset by inflexibility in the level of staffing. It is often difficult to change the size or composition of an in-house systems analysis group quickly or easily, given civil service and budgetary procedures. The build-up in manpower and competence is slow, and once built up, major short-run fluctuations in staff would quickly make retention of a high-quality staff impossible.

But a stable staff size may not correspond to the flow of an agency's analytical needs. In particular, the sudden emergence of systems analysis as needed support for the Planning-Programming-Budgeting System and for the evaluation of new systems, has created a surge in demand for analysts that may be found to exceed the stable ultimate level in many departments. This is a dilemma that has been faced for years by R&D organizations--which is what systems analysis groups are--and has usually been solved by initiating that quantity of R&D per year which can be performed by a group of a size that the organization wishes to support in the long run, with emergency needs handled by outside contracts. Admittedly, if an organization permits the pace of its modernization to be set by the size of the long-run analysis it can justify it is a classic example of the tail wagging the dog, as the cost of self-analysis is usually a very minor part of a departmental program.

NOTE TO CHAPTER 8

[1]Richard E. Neustadt, <u>Presidential Power: The Politics of Leadership</u> (New York: John Wiley & Sons, Inc., 1960), pp. 33-57.

CHAPTER **9** DO WE WANT MORE SYSTEMS

ANALYSIS IN GOVERNMENT?

Several decades ago, commenting on analytical
trends in economics that were then only in their
infancy, J. B. Clark spoke of "the irrational
passion for dispassionate rationality." More
recently Russell Baker poked fun at the systems
ideas in these words:

> We hold these truths to be self-
> provident: that all men are created
> unorganized; that they are endowed by
> their system with certain inalienable
> rights; . . . that, to secure these
> rights, systems are instituted over
> men, deriving their powers from the
> genius of rapid information-retrieval
> techniques; that whenever individuals
> become destructive of these systems,
> it is the rights of these individuals
> to abolish their individuality and to
> reorganize themselves in such forms as
> shall seem most likely to affect the
> system's safety and happiness.[1]

There is indeed a public debate underway as to
the uses of systems analysis in public life. Admittedly,
many reactions to the systems approach are visceral,
and can be set aside as not contributing to a well-
chosen perspective. In responding with cool objectivity,
systems analysis proponents are, in a sense, choosing
their own ground, although it is not clear that they
are objective in their evaluation of their own work
as they would like systems analyses themselves to be.

In common with the rest of mankind, systems analysts are influenced by their work experiences. They become somewhat tool-oriented whereas their customers are problem-oriented in the sense of not preferring one mode of problem-solving over another. Whereas a systems analyst will see the possibility of dealing with a problem area by systems analytical methods he may overlook what the administrator may see, that they are not the only nor necessarily the most practical basis for approaching a problem.

A fundamental question is whether a mode of analytical treatment that requires transforming the object of analysis into the guise of a system is always valid or useful. On balance, there seem to be some subjects for which a system concept is very apt: We speak of communications systems naturally; without elaborate explanation there is little confusion. The system concept fits elsewhere with more strain. Is it not possible that some activities are not systems at all? Is it not possible that a systems approach may sometimes complicate a problem for which very simple techniques give quite adequate answers--or worse, may sometimes obscure the concept of a problem or some aspects of it? Can systems analysis be fitted to a framework that supports society and take a useful place without distorting some aesthetically desirable pattern of that society? Can systems analysis remain a servant?

All in all, systems analysis is largely an approach of using means to achieve objectives or ultimate ends. It has very little to say about ultimate ends, though potentially much to say about intermediate ends, taken in the context of their relevance to ultimate ends. In principle, systems analysis is completely catholic as to the end structure to which it is directed, to the point where it could be used to support the ends of a humanist or a Zen Buddhist. But in practice, systems analysts find some types of ends more tractable than others. These become the typical subjects for systems analysis, although the pressure to force other subjects into a compatible analytical mold is strong and continuous. It does lead systems analysts to inappropriate assumptions as to benefit functions.

At the same time, many of the ends of society
are intermediate, measurable, and clear cut. Here
analysis is on firm ground and can clearly contribute.
Much should be gained from these applications--enough
to counterbalance hesitancy over misapplications, if
there is a clear-eyed view of what system analysis in
government is and can be, both on the part of its
subjects and its practitioners.

Much informed objection to systems analysis is
based on the frequency of obvious and serious defi-
ciencies in the typical analysis: cost functions
obtained in too cavalier a manner, simplistic models
as well as irrelevant measures of benefit, and poor
statements of objectives. A person with a cynical
bent may conclude that no systems analysis is without
serious or fatal flaws somewhere. To protest that is
a matter of degree, while not emotionally satisfying,
is the most accurate response. While some analyses
may be so bad as to be utterly useless, others confirm
or support judgments based principally on other grounds,
while other analyses may be suitable as a principal
basis of judgment. Nitpicking at the run of systems
analyses suggests that the proper response is improvement Proponents of systems analysis would accept
better analyses as a worthy goal, and conclude that
critics whose comments were in this vein were carping
principally at the immaturity of existing methods--
but that both they and the critics worshipped the same
gods.

The methodology of systems analysis is not able
to cope with all problems to which it may be applied.
This is particularly the case with static analytical
methods drawn from the methods of neoclassical
economics. Marginal analysis, in the pattern of microeconomics, assumes a stationary condition. It is not
well-conceived to trace the dynamic response of a
system to changing demand or environment. Growth
in population, changes in technology, depletion of
resources, additions to the capital stock available
to society, changing international, political, and
military considerations, changes in the social
behavior of people, the effects of weather and
agricultural results are forces which will make

certain that we will always be living in a dynamic,
ever - adjusting society. The process of seeking an
optimum is one of striving toward an ever-changing
target rather than a stationary one.

Movement toward optima does not always proceed
in a smooth steady manner. Exaggerated reactions and
overcompensation are characteristic of the behavior
of social organizations. Social systems in particular
often seek an equilibrium that embodies some undesirable
level of pattern. This is at the root of problems of
many underdeveloped countries, and in the United States
certain regions have stabilized into patterns of poverty.
While a tendency toward stability, therefore, is not
always a desirable system characteristic, it is a common one in "natural" systems, which may indeed be an
impediment to implementing changes. Perhaps social
reform may be achievable only by eliminating equilibrium-
restoring feedback of the old system. This may be for
example how an industrial dynamicist would describe the
civil rights movement: Feedback from greater racial
equality may increase the intensity of desire for even
fuller equality--a kind of positive feedback. Without
some positive feedback, the old stabilizing forces would
tend to restore the old equilibrium condition. But as
a new, more acceptable equilibrium condition is approached,
feedback must again become negative or the result is truly
explosive.

Despite the difficulties with stationary concepts
they have some advantages as a basis for systems analysis.
First of all, stationary analysis is much simpler.
Secondly, a stationary, optimizing analysis can describe
the end point toward which dynamic adjustment proceeds.
To the extent that this end point is an optimum, stationary analysis identifies a target for general guidance of operating decisions.

As optimization is one of the principal objectives
of system design, a useful dynamic system concept must
lead to optimization. The system analyst can make an
evaluation of the efficiency of resource use, determine
whether benefit has been maximized in whatever model he
has stabilized by the modification of functional relationships in order to achieve stability. Where there

are several techniques by which stability might be
achieved, an optimization criterion must be used to
choose between them. Given the present state of the
art, there may in fact need to be two parallel models
of the same system--an optimizing model and a stabilization model.

The systems analyst must consider to what extent
stability is itself an objective. It is entirely
possible that a somewhat unstable pattern of behavior
is in fact more efficient than one that is fully
stabilized. The point may be illustrated from inventory theory. An optimal inventory policy is frequently
what is known as an "S s" inventory policy. Small s
refers to the reorder point: When stocks plus back
orders have fallen to this value, an order is placed
sufficient to bring the stock back to the large S level.
As a result, inventory level follows a sawtooth cyclical
fluctuation. Yet this is an optimal inventory policy,
more efficient than one in which inventory levels were
stabilized.

Doubts may also be expressed about system management concepts. From the time of the pyramids, mankind
has had the inner intellectual resources needed to
organize gigantic tasks. World War II was a prime
example of an inherent ability to organize and carry
forward gigantic enterprises that surpassed the experience of any of the participants. Yet it was the obvious
waste, and failures to find best approaches quickly and
efficiently, that provided the impetus to the systems
approach to military problems during World War II.
Following World War II, the circumstances of major
weapon emphasis led the Air Force to be the first
major user of the systems approach, although essential
ingredients had long existed in all the military
services.

As large civilian programs have emerged in recent
years, they too are making use of the system-like concepts. Analytical disciplines to support such efforts
have developed immensely, and are still developing.
There have been demonstrated successes in the analysis
and management of systems. Even if there had not been,
the growing importance of system-like problems would

bring into focus the need to develop and improve
analytical tools for problems of major scope.

At this time my inclination is to give systems
proponents the benefit of the doubt. While work
experience may have given some analysts an unfounded
faith in their methods, it is not likely that such
attitudes are often the result of total ignorance of
other approaches. Systems analysis is not yet a well-
established discipline; relatively few persons are
committed to it by academic training. Indeed, it has
been notorious that systems analytical and operations
research groups have been staffed from widely varied
disciplines--engineering, science, mathematics, economics. Nearly all practitioners have had other analytical experience, even though increasingly there
are persons whose whole career has been systems analysis, and may even have trained for it.

The opposition comes both from persons with some
analytical training, and those without it. Many
attacks on the systems approach are clearly related
to the general attack on science or scientism. The
discomfort of many humanists with a more analytical
world is not news--it is partly the age-old fear of
the unknown. There is, indeed, no reason why analytical approaches cannot be framed to support the goal
structure of humanists. Indeed, the analytically
oriented can argue that to extend analysis is to
reduce the scope of shoddy rationalization in support
of the unsupportable. If analyses seem more often to
exalt material over human values, the humanists are
partly at fault by not advancing their values to serve
as part of the analysts' goal structure.

Forms of analysis have indeed acquired a bad
name from occasional use as a screen to protect positions that honest analysis could not support. The
uses of political economy during the nineteenth century to lend moral support to great social evils are
surely cases in point: The famous "iron law of wages"
held that, in the long run, it was impossible to raise
the wages of the working class above bare subsistence,
as anything more would lead to a population explosion
that would eventually drive wages back down. The

comfort that this specious analysis gave to those inclined to pay low wages undoubtedly contributed to its popularity, and helped earn economics the sobriquet of the "dismal science."

Analysis can surely be bad, and the reaction of nonanalysts to the conclusions analysts draw may often appropriately warn that something is wrong. It is unfortunate that the critics of particular analyses are often at so great a disadvantage in offering criticism. The technical elaborateness of systems analysis accentuates their frustration: Whereas many would feel able to point out a flaw in a simple cost-benefit comparison, to jump upon a full-blown system analysis is to land in a briar patch. Even experienced systems analysts may need to dig deep to uncover analytical flaws, and because the full details of systems analyses are seldom released, the relatively few persons who have the opportunity to dig deeply are seldom devil's advocates. The most strategically placed reviewers in the Federal Government are the examiners in the Bureau of the Budget, who undoubtedly do a great deal to keep the Government intellectually honest. Their focus on direct costs tends to make them less effective vis-à-vis external costs and benefits, without which cost-benefit calculations by a public agency may be no more than a hoax, and which are frequently at the heart of objections to existing analytical efforts.

It seems legitimate to reject--or refuse to act on--an analysis that cannot be explained. Because of their impenetrability, systems analyses are often of this sort. Where the analyst is reduced to asking for approval on faith, his audience is within its rights to judge by whatever means are at its disposal, whether they are confronted with persons able to derive proper conclusions from their evidence, with sets of values they can accept, able to put first things first, and not likely to be blinded by their analytical machinery.

This is a test which many systems analysts fail. It is not an unfair test: It does indeed behoove the systems analyst to obtain the confidence of those who

cannot practically be put in the position of duplica-
ting and verifying in their own terms the results of
his analyses.

The danger in analytical manipulation of society
has been taken as a culture in which science for its
own sake dominates. I was informed by a college
student in colonial costume, operating an eighteenth-
century cordwainer's shop in colonial Williamsburg
that the reason that left and right shoes were made
from identical lasts was the eighteenth-century
passion for symmetry--that an earlier age had shaped
left and right shoes to fit the feet as we do today.
Corns and bunions accepted in the name of enlighten-
ment are perhaps as exquisite an agony as the systems
approach will produce. Perhaps some critics of science
and systems analysis are merely opposed to an analytical
approach to life, or to a society dominated by such
approaches: A relatively unstructured, instinctively
directed, artistically inclined existence can be fun.
There are probably many secret beatniks who feel this
way--and I suspect that more than one systems analyst
feels inclined to join that crowd when he lays down
his slide rule.

THE SYSTEM CONCEPT AND PPBS

Planning-Programming-Budgeting System (PPBS)
is a program-oriented method of financial planning of
government operations. It involves structuring governmental activities according to similarity of objectives
or results, and is composed, therefore, of elements
which are comparable as to the benefits sought. Where
package elements are in some sense meaningfully associated, packaging contributes to rational decision-
making. For example, if a package were so composed
that the elements of its internal structure could be
evaluated vis-à-vis each other, without taking account
of things excluded from the package, there would be a
simplification of the decision-making structure.

The time perspective of a PPBS concept is also
helpful. The benefits from programs are often further in the future than the time of spending. Neglect-
ing the time difference is not likely to ease rational

decision-making. Program packaging highlights the
need for and enhances the possibilities of life-cycle
analysis of a program including the period of investment and the period of benefit.

The philosophies of PPBS and systems analysis have
much in common. Being composed of a number of semi-
autonomous parts which interact with each other to
achieve movement toward common objectives, PPBS is
properly called a system. In the most formal sense,
the design objective of PPBS is a Federal budget in
which funds are allocated among major programs and
within the structure of each program. The objective
of PPBS is to achieve an allocation of funds that
most effectively advances the broad mix of Federal
Government objectives, by allocating support to programs developed analytically. The means used include
interprogram comparisons of the net change in benefits
that result from shifting funds from one program to
another.

In analysis in support of PPBS, it will occasionally seem appropriate to treat an agency of government
and the part of society with which it interacts as a
system. An operating agency is often one that has
responsibility for the resources which are used to
produce a benefit. An example is the National Park
System, in which the parks are operated by the system
and the benefits are received principally by the users
of the system. Such agencies must, to be sure, take
account of the externalities on both the cost and
benefit side, but most resources used are under direct
control. On the other hand, a regulatory agency has
almost no direct responsibility for the resources used
to produce a benefit, these being in the hands of the
group which it regulates. It influences the manner in
which resources are used and the particular benefits
produced by its industry. These regulations frequently
take the form of constraints within which those regu-
lated are free to pursue a profit-maximizing behavior.
Thus, except for the rather small amount of resources
used in the act of regulation itself, all costs and
all benefits are external.

Examining the responsibilities of either type of
agency in the system-analytical context, would imply

a re-examination of objectives, a model, and design.
of the system from a selection of possible technologies,
perhaps including some novel ones. Such an effort is
closely akin to what many organizations attempt through
planning. As a framework for program analysis, PPBS
depends for its effectiveness on analytical techniques
that are highly similar, if not identical, to those
used in systems analysis. Many of the problems and
caveats stressed in the preceding chapters are equally
applicable to PPBS. But PPBS does not require a well-
developed system model. Government undertakes a multi-
tude of services, regulatory and other activities, many
of which are sufficiently independent in resources used
and benefits produced that it is not clear that there
would be any advantage in attempting to consider them
as parts of a system. As program aggregation is pushed
further and further, at a certain point the democratic
political process becomes the dominant means for interprogram comparisons; no one believes that systems analysis will replace this process.

     It is at this point that the contrast between
PPBS and systems analysis is most marked. A systems
analysis is commonly directed at a single highly
integrated system, directed at objectives that strongly
interact, or where actions to attain the objectives
would interact. The structure of government contains
many activities legitimately but not easily defined
as systems in this context: manpower development,
pollution control, public health, education, transportation, defense, and internal revenue. Such program
elements, as parts of program packages, can often be
effectively treated as self-contained systems. These
programs do not follow organizational lines in all
cases. A successful packaging of programs is likely
to display in juxtaposition a mix of activities that
in fact may be administered separately, although
similar in objective. There is probably no better
example than the transportation-related activities of
the Federal Government. Systems analysis may be a
technically successful approach to unified analysis
of interdepartmental programs.

THE STRATEGY OF SYSTEMS ANALYSIS

Also of considerable importance is the effect that the manner in which systems analysis is conducted may have on the prospects for plan implementation. PPBS and any systems analyses that support it are planning exercises, and often plans are not translated into action. City planning has an extensive record of this sort, and one that may be particularly relevant to PPBS, as it illustrates the difficulties of implementing plans through a political process. At present the record is not clear as to the use that will be made of PPBS and systems analysis in government. It is never certain, a priori, how deeply any form of planning will penetrate into the heart of an organization: to what extent it will become part of an organization's mechanism for management and control.

Many proponents of PPBS have assumed that what is structured in PPBS will become translated into reality. With the best of intentions this may not be easy. The complexity of government objectives is obvious enough, as is the organizational complexity inherent in the Federal structure. That extraordinary problems of achieving plan implementation arise from this structure was the thrust of Harry S. Truman's famous remark, quoted by Richard Neustadt, "Poor Ike, he'll say 'do this, do that,' and nothing will happen," suggesting that the implementation structure in military services was substantially more automatic.[2]

A great deal might be said about various organizational positions for a systems analytical capability in support of PPBS. On the one hand, a choice might be made that will produce the best possible analysis judged in the abstract. Yet the impact of such an analysis may be minimal. There are, in fact, arguments for close liaison with top management (so that it will be aware of the most vital objectives of the organization) and with lower echelons (where it will have the greatest impact on the choices made in the first round of planning). Having systems analytical capabilities at several levels--as has been done in the Department of Defense--may be a better solution than having a single systems analysis group.

The germinal point for the initial development
of an element of an over-all plan and the necessary
technical information is likely to be fairly low in
the hierarchy of the organization, with the over-all
plan being the consolidation of the products of a
bottom-up process. There are a number of reasons:
One is that actually in an on-going organization,
most decisions as to scope and nature of activities
are highly similar to routine decisions that have
been made many times before and have been delegated
downward in the organization. In the language of
Herbert A. Simon, most decisions are <u>programmed</u>.[3]

That bottom-up planning is not likely to result
in fundamental changes in an organization, or its
concept of its functions, is inherent in the concentration that operating management must apply to on-
going operations. Management which is thoroughly
immersed in operations tends to see its future tasks
as simple extensions of those it is already performing. The typical result will be of the type scorned
by Thoreau when he said, "Make no small plans; they
have no power to stir men's souls." Clearly, major
changes in organizational strategy will most often
be generated by the top management or by a staff
which is somewhat isolated from the pressure of
operations. It is groups of this sort that are in
the strongest position to take a systems approach to
the over-all organization. Even in the milieu of
bottom-up planning some central guidance as to objectives and goals is necessary. In the words of Bureau
of the Budget Circular 66-3:[4]

> The entire system must operate within the
> framework of over-all policy guidance--from
> the President to the agency head, and from
> the agency head to his central planning,
> programming and budgeting staffs and to his
> line managers.

The involvement of the line organization in
reaching decisions as to specific steps that they
are later to implement is likely to be a major factor
influencing the degree of implementation. It is,
after all, the operation of the line organization

that produces the benefits seen in a plan. The
separation of plan creation and implementation is a
poor way to enlist wholehearted support by the operating management. Difficulties created by such a
separation--resentment, unreality, misinterpretation--
often seriously reduce the degree to which plans are
implemented. Thus the trade-off between degree of
implementation and what it is that is implemented is
intertwined with the scope of participation in the
process of plan creation. Broadening the participation to the operating group is, furthermore, likely
to affect all phases of a plan from objectives to
specific programs.

Participation has often been used effectively
as a means for obtaining commitment throughout an
organization. At the minimum, a manager may be asked
to propose what he can accomplish with given resources,
on a given schedule. If his proposal is accepted as
part of the plan, he has a strengthened commitment to
meet the goals he has set for himself. These goals
may not, however, be those that a headquarters staff
group would have selected, or would be indicated by
a systems analysis. The manager may perhaps be induced
to change his goals in the light of the views of his
staff, but at a certain point an irreducible difference in views as to what may be accomplished may be
left. Surely the best resolution of these differences
must take account of the manager's personal characteristics, and the general organizational climate. Will
plans be documents that he strives wholeheartedly to
implement? Does the plan give him sufficient control
over resources to achieve his goals? How does he
interact with others in the managerial hierarchy who
may also be seeking change influenced by PPBS?

Plan implementation depends on the provisions
made for monitoring performance according to a plan.
If there are mechanisms by which deviations become
known to top management which lead it to express
concern or take proper corrective measures, lower-
echelon management will endeavor to meet plan objectives. Feedback of this sort cannot be obtained
unless the plan has specified time-phased results
in explicit terms. Vaguely stated planning goals,

such as "increased output" or targets without a specified date, can be used only for imprecise comparisons
of plan and performance. Thus, the intent to achieve
implementation imposes requirements on the generators
of plans for a volume of detail that carries planning
much further than might otherwise be necessary. Indeed,
the significance of the a priori choice of detail may
not be very great--it is merely necessary that some
choice be made to fulfill the need for monitoring
implementation. One result of planning carried to
this extreme may be an excessively restrictive and
inflexible program. When the time to act arrives,
the manager may have persuasive reasons for taking
another route, though in doing so he creates a deviation from plan that must be explained--and it may not
be worth it.

The above is only one of several difficult conflicts between detail and flexibility. Another is the
scope of the plan. The term "zero-base budget" has
been used to describe a budget in which every item is
justified in its entirety, as opposed to justification
only of incremental changes from the last budget.
Justifying only incremental changes is comparable to
the concept of marginality in that only increments of
benefits and increments of cost are compared without
taking into account the whole corpus for which the
increment is an adjustment. Despite the advantage
of reduced analytical problems there are dangers in
incrementalism. While improvement in an organization's
program might be sought through incremental steps, the
process may be even slower than political, administrative, or technological problems would permit. Further,
not all program alternatives are related to each other
by smooth functions, such that the transition may be
made from one to another in a series of increments.

While zero-base budgeting would seem to minimize
the dangers of incrementalism, a zero-base budgeting
may be too expensive to justify as an annual exercise.
Even in the Department of Defense, a small proportion
of elements had to be analyzed in such depth when the new
program package budget was first used in 1961.

PPBS AND THE POLITICAL PROCESS

The position of the Executive has probably been
strengthened vis-à-vis Congress by the depth of the
planning structure provided by PPBS. To the extent
that PPBS work is well done, the result may be a
shift in power toward the Executive Branch--otherwise
Congress will be increasingly in the position of
rejecting well-conceived Executive Branch proposals
out of hand. In the longer run, Congress may react
by creating a comparable analytical capability so
that it may confront the Executive with alternative
program structures, with a comparable analytical
support.

PPBS is essentially proposed as a better way to
create plans, and on the whole it seems easier to
create plans where the constraints on the exercise
are those of the planner's choosing than to implement
them. It may yet be asked whether PPBS produces a
more implementable plan, or plans that--in the context
of existing organizations--are more likely to be implemented. The power of the top of a bureaucracy to
change an organization is limited, as Franklin Roosevelt
knew when he said, "Trying to change the Navy is like
punching a featherbed."[5] Ultimately, the implementation of PPBS-generated plans may depend on whether
PPBS becomes principally a top-level staff activity
or a staff-supported function of line management.
And make no mistake: As initially implemented, PPBS
is principally a staff activity--first efforts were
largely the efforts of specialized PPBS staff groups
It is an over-simplification to equate the plans of
a staff with those of top management, let alone the
line organization.

NOTES TO CHAPTER 9

[1]The New York Times, April 13, 1967.

[2]Richard E. Neustadt, Presidential Power: The
Politics of Leadership (New York: John Wiley &
Sons, Inc., 1960), p. 9.

[3]Herbert A. Simon, The New Science of Management Decision (New York: Harper and Row, 1960), pp. 14-20.

[4]Neustadt, op. cit.

[5]Quoted by Neustadt, ibid., p. 42.

APPENDIX

AN EARLY EXAMPLE OF A SYSTEMS APPROACH*

In the fall of 1877, Edison began experimenting with incandescent lights. There is no evidence which explains why he turned to the incandescent light at that time. There were many inventors working on arc lights and incandescent lights, and presumably Edison was curious about the possibilities in electric lighting.

The plan he evolved was striking in its breadth and originality. He decided, first of all, that he was not interested in arc lighting. The nature of the arc light limited it to street lighting and other large-space lighting. Edison knew that over 90 per cent of the revenues of the gas companies came from home and office illumination. Here the arc light could not be used.

In choosing the incandescent light over the arc light, Edison was putting aside the technical advance that had brought the arc light to the commercial stage. Very little of that technical advance could be applied to incandescent lighting. Instead of using it as a foundation on which to build, Edison would have to achieve comparable technical advance in a separate field. To develop an electric light for use in homes, he could not merely replace the lighting element in the arc-lighting system. He would need to design a new dynamo, one with high efficiency to compensate for the low efficiency of the incandescent light and with a constant-potential characteristic. The arc-lighting dynamo had a constant-current characteristic-- the current output tended to be the same regardless of the number of lamps connected to the dynamo--which was suitable for a series but not for a parallel system. Edison wanted to use the parallel system because it permitted each user to operate any light independently of the others. The series system, where all lights are turned on and off at once, was satisfactory for street lighting but not for home lighting. Protection against

*Abstracted by permission of the publishers from Harold C. Passer, The Electrical Manufacturers, 1875-1900 (Cambridge, Mass.: Harvard University Press; copyright 1953 by the President and Fellows of Harvard College); Chapter VII, "The Edison System".

short circuits, not needed in a constant-current system, and sockets and switches would also be required.
The introduction of the electric circuit into homes
instead of confining it to the streets meant that
the voltages used would have to be much lower than
those permissible with the arc light. Low voltages
raised problems of energy loss in transmission.
These led to the complicated transmission networks
which were quite foreign to the simple series circuits
of arc lighting.

Edison's conception of the problem before him is
shown by entries he made in one of his notebooks about
this same time. "Object, Edison to effect exact imi-
tation of all done by gas so as to replace lighting
by gas by lighting by electricity...Edison's great
effort not to make a large light or a blinding light
but a small light having the mildness of gas."

In deciding to try to invent an incandescent
light, Edison was attempting to solve a problem which
many scientists thought to be insoluble. It was
believed that the subdivision of the electric light
was theoretically impossible in the same sense that
the construction of a perpetual-motion machine is
theoretically impossible.

An English scientist, Professor Sylvanus Thompson,
in lecturing on the problem of the subdivision of the
electric light in 1878 stated that "any system depending on incandescence will fail." Sir William Preece
lectured before the Royal United Service Institution
on February 15, 1879, where he said: "It is, however,
easily shown (and that is by the application of perfectly definite and well-known scientific laws) that
in a circuit where the electro-motive force is constant,
and we insert additional lamps, then when these lamps
are joined up in one circuit, i.e., in series, the
light varies inversely as the square of the number
of the lamps in the circuit and that joined up in
multiple arc, the light diminishes as the cube of
the number inserted. Hence a subdivision of the
electric light is an absolute ignis factuus."

Edison saw that it was possible to increase the
amount of current and solve the problem. His boldness

in undertaking the impossible was based on his own
profound understanding of fundamental electrical laws
and his ability to apply these laws to a practical
problem. He knew he wanted a small light which could
be independently controlled. Independent control
implied a parallel circuit where, with a constant-
voltage generator, the current units could be multi-
plied as desired. But the increase in current could
mean either heavy energy loss in transmission or excessive copper cost. To avoid these, the light would
have to be of high resistance. That conclusion is
easily reached by an elementary application of Ohm's
law. But in Edison's time, it was an important achieve-
ment which placed Edison far ahead of the other incandescent light inventors and scientists and led him to
develop a commercially successful electric-lighting
system. The concept of the high-resistance lamp is
a perfect illustration of that blend of technical
and economic reasoning which underlay the successful
innovation in the first years of the electrical manufacturing industry.

On October 21, 1879, the first successful incandescent electric light was made and tested. On December 31 of that same year, Edison held the first public
demonstration of his lighting system at Menlo Park.
He lighted the laboratory, the office, the streets of
Menlo Park, and some adjoinging houses with over fifty
lamps. Hundreds of people from New York and elsewhere
traveled via the Pennsylvania Railroad to witness the
demonstration.

The completion of the basic inventions permitted
emphasis on further development and improvement. When
the first central station was projected, the principal
technical characteristics of the system had to be chosen.
What were to be the values of the electrical constants
in the commercial lighting system? The problem here
was to decide on the lamp resistance, the circuit
voltage, the conductor sizes, and the energy loss to
be permitted. In view of the difficulties of making
high-resistance lamps and the dangers of high voltage
in the home, Edison decided to use 100-ohm lamps and
100-volt circuits. The transmission energy loss was

to be about 10 per cent, a figure which permitted a reasonably small copper investment at 110 volts. These decisions implied the economical size for a district served by one central station--about one square mile.

Edison's clear understanding of Ohm's law and its application to the problem of economizing copper costs and transmission losses led him to choose correct values of voltage, lamp resistance, and conductor size. Edison himself did not carry out the lengthy calculations involved in making these choices. He had neither adequate mathematical training nor sufficient time. The calculating was turned over to Edison's mathematician, F. R. Upton, who was able to apply mathematical techniques in solving the problems. Because Upton's education reflected the state of scientific knowledge, Edison had to reeducate to a true understanding of electrical laws. At first Upton could not understand why Edison wanted a lamp of high resistance. Years later Upton commented: "I cannot imagine why I ·could not see the elementary facts in 1878 and 1879 more clearly than I did. I came to Mr. Edison a trained man, a postgraduate at Princeton; with a year's experience in Helmholz's laboratory; with a working knowledge of calculus and a mathematical turn of mind."

When Upton had learned Edison's use of Ohm's law, he could compute the most economical conductor sizes by taking account of copper costs, energy costs, and interest costs. Here he applied calculus to an ordinary minimization problem and worked out a number of solutions depending on various assumed conditions.

With his technical problems on the way to solution, Edison could turn to his marketing problem. He decided to solve this in the most direct way possible--by establishing a central station in New York City to demonstrate the economic worth of his lighting system.

Edison chose to place his first commercial central station on Pearl Street in lower Manhattan. This location brought the Wall Street financial district within the area to be served by the station. Edison wanted to prove to the financial community that his lighting system was practical, economical, and much superior to gas.

The size of the Pearl Street station, that is, its generating capacity measured by the number of lights it could serve, was determined on the basis of data obtained by Edison's men. They canvassed the district thoroughly to learn the number of gas jets burning at each hour up to 3 A.M. A house-to-house survey was made later which provided information on the number of gas jets in each building. The data obtained in these surveys also helped in planning the transmission network. A miniature network of conductors was constructed with a battery serving for the central station and with resistors for the lights. Careful studies were made of the voltage conditions in the model network, using various sizes and arrangements of the conductors.

Edison planned to set the price of electric energy equivalent to the price of gas. He apparently reached this decision after one of his surveys in which the gas consumers were asked whether or not they would take the electric light if its price were the same as gas. Users of all but 850 of the 16,000 gas jets in the Pearl Street district answered in the affirmative.

At the formation of Edison General Electric in 1889, Edison withdrew almost completely from the electrical manufacturing industry. After 1886, he had not actively directed the operation of the machine works and the lamp works, but he had kept his controlling interest in both firms. He gave his reasons for selling his electrical manufacturing enterprises in a letter which he wrote to Henry Villard in 1890. "I have been under a desperate strain for money for twenty-two years, and when I sold out, one of the greatest inducements was the sum of cash received, which I thought I could always have on hand, so as to free my mind from financial stress, and thus enable me to go ahead in the technical field." Edison went on to say that he was no longer interested in electric lighting and that "working day and night to advance efficiency from 80 to 85 per cent is an absurdity."

Thus, by 1890, Edison was ready to turn to new fields of endeavor. He had achieved the goal he set

for himself in 1878--to develop an incandescent
electric-lighting system--and he had seen that system
attain widespread use.

BIBLIOGRAPHY

SELECTED BIBLIOGRAPHY

Abt Associates. "Survey of the State of the Art:
    Social, Political and Economic Models and Simu-
    lations." Technology and the National Economy,
    Appendix, Vol. V, pp. V-204 to V-250. Report
    by the U.S. National Commission on Technology,
    Automation and Economic Progress, February 1966.

Affel, Herman A., Jr. "System Engineering." Inter-
    national Research and Development, No. 35 (No-
    vember 1964), pp. 18-26.

American Academy of Political and Social Science.
    (Annals.) Social Goals and Indicators for a
    Great Society, 1967.

Arrow, Kenneth J. Social Choice and Individual
    Values. New York: John Wiley & Sons, Inc.,
    1951.

Ashby, W. Ross. An Introduction to Cybernetics.
    New York: John Wiley & Sons, Inc.(Science
    Editions), 1963.

Asher, Harold. Cost-Quantity Relationships in the
    Airframe Industry. Report R-291. Santa Mon-
    ica, Calif.: The RAND Corporation, July 1956.

Bauer, Raymond A., ed. Social Indicators. Cam-
    bridge, Mass.: Massachusetts Institute of
    Technology Press, 1966.

Baumol, William J. Welfare Economics and the Theory
    of the State. 2nd ed. Cambridge, Mass.: Har-
    vard University Press, 1965.

Berelson, Bernard A., and Steiner, Gary A. Human
    Behavior: An Inventory of Scientific Findings.
    New York: Harcourt, Brace, and World, Inc.,
    1964. "Problem-Solving and Creative Thinking,"
    pp. 200-208.

Black, Alan. "Optimizing Density of Development
    with Respect to Transportation Cost." Tri-
    State Transportation Commission Interim Tech-
    nical Report 4040-3243, June 1966, 35 pp.,
    mimeographed.

Black, Guy. Cost Considerations in the Evaluation
     of Electronic Countermeasure Systems. Report
     EDL-M109. Mountain View, Calif.: Electronic
     Defense Laboratory, April, 1957.

Black, Guy. "Synthetic Method of Cost Analysis in
     Agricultural Marketing Firms." Journal of Farm
     Economics, Vol. 37 (May 1955), pp. 270-279.

Black, Guy. "Systems Analysis in Government Opera-
     tions." Management Science, Vol. 14, No. 2
     (October 1967), pp. B-41 to B-57.

Black, Guy, and Proschan, Frank. "On Optimal Redun-
     dancy." Operations Research, Vol. 7, No. 5
     (September-October 1959), pp. 581-588.

Boulding, K.E. "The Ethics of Rational Decision."
     Management Science, Vol. 12, No. 8 (February
     1966), pp. B-161 to B-169.

Bressler, R.G., Jr. "Research Determination of
     Economics of Scale." Journal of Farm Econom-
     ics, Vol. XXVII, No. 3 (August 1945), pp. 526-
     539.

Brewster, John M. Comparative Economies of Differ-
     ent Types of Cottonseed Oil Mills and Their
     Effects on Oil Supplies, Prices and Returns to
     Growers. U.S. Agricultural Marketing Service.
     Marketing Research Report No. 54. Washington,
     D.C.: Government Printing Office, February
     1954.

Brown, Harrison; Bonner, James; and Weir, John.
     The Next Hundred Years. New York: The Viking
     Press, 1963.

Carlson, Sune. A Study on the Pure Theory of Pro-
     duction. New York: Kelley and Millman, 1956.

Chenery, Hollis B. "Engineering Production Func-
     tions." Quarterly Journal of Economics, Vol.
     63 (November 1949), pp. 507-531.

Chenery, Hollis B., and Clark, Paul G. (Chapter
     5.) "Empirical Bases for Interindustry Models."
     Interindustry Economics. New York: John Wiley
     & Sons, Inc., 1959, pp. 137-156.

Chestnut, Harold. System Engineering Tools. New
     York: John Wiley & Sons, Inc., 1965.

Churchman, C. West; Ackoff, Russell L.; and Arnoff,
    E. Leonard. Introduction to Operations Re-
    search. New York: John Wiley & Sons, Inc.,
    1957.

Coleman, James S. "The Possibility of a Social
    Welfare Function." American Economic Review,
    Vol. LVI, No. 5 (December 1966), pp. 1105-1122.

Committee on Economic Development. Budgeting for
    National Objectives. New York: Committee on
    Economic Development, 1966.

Cyert, Richard M., and March, James F. A Behav-
    ioral Theory of the Firm. Englewood Cliffs,
    N.J.: Prentice Hall, 1963. Chapter 3, "Organ-
    izational Goals," pp. 26-36.

Dalkey, Norman, and Helmer, Olaf. "An Experimental
    Application of the Delphi Method to the Use of
    Experts." Management Science, Vol. 9, No. 3
    (April 1963), pp. 458-467.

Dean, Joel. Statistical Determination of Costs,
    With Special Reference to Marginal Costs.
    Studies in Business Administration, Vol. VII,
    No. 1. Chicago: University of Chicago, 1936.

Dean, Joel. "Decentralization and Intra-Company
    Pricing." Harvard Business Review, Vol. 33,
    No. 4 (July-August 1955), pp. 65-74.

Dooley, Arch R. "Interpretations of PERT." Har-
    vard Business Review, Vol. 42, No. 2 (March-
    April 1964), pp. 160-172.

Dorfman, Robert, ed. Measuring Benefits of Govern-
    ment Investment. Washington, D.C.: Brookings
    Institution, 1965.

Dorfman, Robert; Samuelson, Paul A.; and Solow, R.
    M. Linear Programming and Economic Analysis.
    New York: McGraw-Hill, 1958.

Enke, Stephen, ed. Defense Management. Englewood
    Cliffs, N.J.: Prentice Hall, 1967.

Fisher, Franklin M. The Identification Problem in
    Econometrics. New York: McGraw-Hill, 1966.

Fisher, G.H. Derivation of Estimating Relation-
     ships: An Illustrative Example. Memorandum
     RM-3366-PR. Santa Monica, Calif.: The RAND
     Corporation, November 1962.

Forrester, J.W. "Industrial Dynamics: A Major
     Breakthrough for Decision Makers." Harvard
     Business Review, Vol. 36, No. 4 (July-August
     1958), pp. 37-66.

Gregory, Robert H., and Van Horn, Richard L. Auto-
     matic Data-Processing Systems: Principles and
     Procedures. San Francisco: Wadsworth Publish-
     ing Co., Inc., 1960.

Haldi, John. "Internal Markets as a Means to
     Greater Efficiency in the Defense Department."
     Internal Note N-77, Institute for Defense
     Analysis, September 20, 1963.

Hall, Arthur D. A Methodology for Systems Engin-
     eering. New York: D. Van Nostrand Co., 1962.

Hammerberg, D.O.; Parker, L.W.; and Bressler, R.G.,
     Jr. Efficiency of Milk Marketing in Connec-
     ticut: Supply and Price Interrelationships
     for Fluid Milk Markets. Bulletin 237. Storrs,
     Connecticut: University of Connecticut, Febru-
     ary 1942.

Hanoch, Giora. "Personal Earnings and Investment
     in Schooling." Unpublished Ph.D. disserta-
     tion, University of Chicago, August 1965.

Hare, Van Court, Jr. "Systems Analysis." Chapter
     5 in Vol. II of Progress in Operations Research.
     Edited by David B. Hertz and Roger T. Eddison.
     New York: John Wiley & Sons, Inc., 1964, pp.
     125-158.

Hitch, Charles J., and McKean, Ronald N. The Econ-
     omics of Defense in the Nuclear Age. Cam-
     bridge, Mass.: Harvard University Press, 1960.

Hitch, Charles J. "Economics and Military Opera-
     tions Research." Review of Economics and
     Statistics, Vol. XL, No. 3 (August 1958).

Johnson, Richard A.; Kast, Fremont E.; and Rosenz-
    weig, James E. The Theory and Management of
    Systems. 2nd ed. New York: McGraw-Hill,
    1967.

Kadet, Jordan, and Frank, B.N.   "PERT for the Engin-
    eer." I.E.E.E. Spectrum, November 1964, pp.
    131-137.

Krupp, Sherman R.   "Equilibrium Theory in Economic
    and in Functional Analysis as Types of Explana-
    tion." Functionalism in the Social Sciences.
    Monograph No. 5. Edited by Don Martindale.
    Philadelphia, Pa.: The American Academy of
    Political and Social Science, February 1965,
    pp. 65-83.

Lange, Oskar. Wholes and Parts: A General Theory
    of System Behavior. New York: Pergamon
    Press, 1965.

Lanning, J. Halcombe, and Battin, Richard H.   Ran-
    dom Processes in Automatic Control. New York:
    McGraw-Hill, 1956.

Lazzaro, Victor, ed. Systems and Procedures: A
    Handbook for Business and Industry. Engle-
    wood Cliffs, N.J.: Prentice Hall, Inc., 1959.

Machol, Robert E., ed. Systems Engineering Hand-
    book. New York: McGraw-Hill, 1965.

MacCrimmon ,K.R., and Ryavc, C.A. "An Analytical
    Study of the PERT Assumptions." Memorandum
    RM-3408-PR. Santa Monica, Calif.: The RAND
    Corporation, December 1962.

Manheim, Karl. Man and Society in an Age of Recon-
    struction: Studies in Modern Social Struc-
    ture. Translated by Edward Shils. New York:
    Harcourt, Brace, and World, Inc., 1940.

March, James G., and Simon, Herbert A. Organiza-
    tions. New York: John Wiley & Sons, Inc.,
    1958.

Markowitz, H.M. Portfolio Selection. Cowles
    Foundation Monograph 16. New York: John
    Wiley & Sons, Inc., 1959.

McKean, Ronald N. Efficiency in Government Through Systems Analysis. New York: John Wiley & Sons, Inc., 1958. (Chapter 2, "The Criterion Problem.")

Miller, Robert W. Schedule, Cost, and Profit Control with PERT. New York: McGraw-Hill, 1963.

Morganstern, Oskar. On the Accuracy of Economic Observations. Princeton, N.J.: Princeton University Press, 1963.

Morrison, E.J. "Defense Systems Management: The 375 Series." California Management Review, Vol. IX, No. 4 (1967), pp. 17-28.

National Planning Association. State Projections to 1975: A Quantitative Analysis of Economic and Demographic Changes. Report 65-11. Washington, D.C.: National Planning Association, 1965.

Nelson, James R., ed. Marginal Price Costing in Practice. Englewood Cliffs, N.J.: Prentice Hall, Inc., 1964.

Nerlove, Marc. Estimation and Identification of Cobb-Douglas Production Functions. Chicago: Rand McNally, 1965.

Neustadt, Richard E. Presidential Power: The Politics of Leadership. New York: John Wiley & Sons, Inc., 1960.

Novick, David, ed. Program Budgeting: Program Analysis and the Federal Budget. Washington, D.C.: Government Printing Office, 1964.

Pelz, Donald C., and Andrews, Frank M. "Evaluation of Performance." Appendix A in Scientists in Organization. New York: John Wiley & Sons, Inc., 1966, pp. 261-270.

Pierce, J.R. Symbols, Signals, and Noise. New York: Harper and Brothers, 1961.

Pirie, N.W. "Orthodox and Unorthodox Methods of Meeting World Food Needs." Scientific American, Vol. 216, No. 2 (February 1967), pp. 27-36.

Quade, E.S., ed. Analysis for Military Decisions.
    Report R-387-PR. Santa Monica, Calif.: The
    RAND Corporation, November 1964.

Quandt, Richard E. "Some Perspectives on Gravity
    Models." Studies in Travel Demand. Prince-
    ton, N.J.: Mathematica, 1965, pp. 33-46.
    (Prepared for Northeast Corridor Transporta-
    tion Project, U.S. Department of Commerce,
    Contract C-247-65 [Neg].)

Quandt, Richard E., and Baumol, W.J. The Abstract
    Mode Model: Theory and Measurement. North-
    east Corridor Transportation Project Techni-
    cal Paper No. 4. Washington, D.C.: U.S.
    Department of Transportation, June 1966.

Rice, Dorothy P. Estimating the Cost of Illness.
    U.S. Department of Health, Education, and Wel-
    fare, Health Economic Series, No. 6. Washing-
    ton, D.C.: U.S. Government Printing Office,
    1966.

Roberts, Edward B. "Facts and Folklore in Research
    and Development Management." Industrial Man-
    agement Review, Vol. 8, No. 2 (Spring 1967),
    pp. 5-18.

Rogers, Everett M. The Diffusion of Innovations.
    New York: The Free Press of Glencoe, 1962.

Schelling, Thomas C. The Strategy of Conflict.
    (Galaxy Book edition.) New York: Oxford
    University Press, 1963.

Sen, A.K. "A Possibility Theorem of Majority De-
    cisions." Econometrica, Vol. 34, No. 2 (April
    1966), pp. 491-499.

Simon, Herbert A. The New Science of Management
    Decision. New York: Harper and Row, 1960.

Smithies, Arthur. The Budgetary Process in the
    United States. New York: McGraw-Hill, 1955,
    pp. 229-263.

State of Illinois. Chicago Area Transportation
    Study, Final Report. Vol. IV, July 1960.

Stedry, Andrew C.   "A Mathematical Model of a Bud-
     get Control System."   Chapter 2 in Budgetary
     Control and Cost Behavior. Englewood Cliffs,
     N.J.: Prentice Hall, 1960, pp. 17-42.

Stigler, George J. The Theory of Price. New York:
     The Macmillan Co., 1946.

Svenson, Arthur L.   "Management Systems and the Ex-
     ception Principle." Systems and Procedures
     Journal, Vol. 15, No. 4 (July-August 1964),
     pp. 44-51.

Taylor, Graeme M., and Rea, Robert H.   "The C-5A
     Concept Formulation: A Case Study in Weapon
     System Acquisition." In Perspectives in
     Defense Management. Washington, D.C.: Indus-
     trial College of the Armed Forces, May 1967.

Theil, Henri. Linear Aggregation of Economic Rela-
     tions. Amsterdam: North Holland Publishing
     Co., 1965.

Theil, Henri; Boot, John C. G.; and Kloek, Teun.
     "The Statistical Specification of Economic
     Relations." Chapter 12 in Operations Research
     and Quantitative Economics. New York: McGraw-
     Hill, 1965, pp. 214-236.

U.S. Air Force Systems Command. Systems Management:
     Systems Program Office Manual. AFSCM375-3.
     Washington, D.C.: Andrews Air Force Base,
     June 15, 1964.

U.S. Air Force Systems Command. Systems Management:
     Systems Program Management Procedures.
     AFSCM375-4. Washington, D.C.: Andrews Air
     Force Base, June 1965.

U.S. Bureau of the Budget. Planning-Programming
     Budgeting. Bulletin 66-3. Washington, D.C.:
     U.S. Bureau of the Budget, October 12, 1965.

U.S. Commission on Organization of the Executive
     Branch of the Government. Budgeting and
     Accounting: A Report to the Congress.
     Washington, D.C.: U.S. Government Printing
     Office, February 1949, pp. 8-12.

U.S. Department of Health, Education, and Welfare.
   Disease Control Programs: Arthritis. Program
   Analysis 1966-1. Washington, D.C.: U.S. Gov-
   ernment Printing Office, September 1966.

U.S. National Aeronautics and Space Administration.
   NASA--PERT in Facilities Project Management.
   Washington, D.C.: U.S. Government Printing
   Office, March 1965.

U.S. National Aeronautics and Space Administration.
   PERT Handbook and Companion Cost System.
   Report NPC-101. Washington, D.C.: U.S. Gov-
   ernment Printing Office, October 30, 1962.

U.S. Treasury Department. Systems and Procedures:
   A Notebook for the Systems Man. Publication
   460 (2-63.) Washington, D.C.: U.S. Government Printing Office, February 1963.

Vickrey, William. "Utility, Strategy, and Social
   Decision Rules." Quarterly Journal of Economics, Vol. 74 (November 1960), pp. 507-535.

Weille, Jan de. Quantifications of Road User Sav-
   ings. World Bank Occasional Paper No. 2.
   Washington, D.C.: International Bank for
   Reconstruction and Development, 1966.

Wildavsky, Aaron, and Hammond, Arthur. "Comprehensive Versus Incremental Budgeting in the
   Department of Agriculture." Administrative
   Science Quarterly, Vol. 10, No. 3 (December
   1965), pp. 321-346.

Williams, J.D. The Compleat Strategist. Revised
   ed. New York: McGraw-Hill, 1966.

Wilson, E. Bright, Jr. An Introduction to Scientific Research. New York: McGraw-Hill, 1952.

INDEX

INDEX

ABOUT THE AUTHOR

Guy Black is Senior Staff Scientist in the Program of Policy Studies in Science and Technology at The George Washington University, Washington, D. C. From 1965 to 1967 he served as Executive Secretary of the President's Committee on the Economic Impact of Defense and Disarmament and as a member of the staff of the Council of Economic Advisers. Prior to this he was employed by Sylvania Electronic Systems as a systems engineer and as a staff specialist in planning and also served on the staff of the Giannini Foundation at the University of California, where he did research in consumer behavior, marketing organization, and transportation.

Dr. Black has been a consultant to the Electronic Industries Association, the Board of Economic Advisers to the Governor of Massachusetts, and the National Planning Association. He is currently a Research Affiliate of the Sloan School of Management at Massachusetts Institute of Technology and a member of the National Academy of Sciences, National Academy of Engineering Panel on Science, Technology, and Regional Economic Development.

Dr. Black studied at Harvard University and received a doctorate in economics from the University of Chicago in 1951.